ULTIMATE JUICES

For Healthy Living

BRIDGET JONES

Acknowledgment: thank you to Magimix for providing invaluable advice and the juicing equipment for testing the recipes.

Published in 2001 by Caxton Editions
20 Bloomsbury Street
London WC1B 3JH
a member of the Caxton Publishing Group

Designed and produced for Caxton Editions
by Open Door Limited
Langham, Rutland

Setting and layout: Richard Booth
Digital imagery © copyright PhotoDisc Inc.
Film production: GA Graphics, Stamford, UK

Title: Ultimate Juices
ISBN: 1 84067 352 4

Printed and bound by CTPS

ULTIMATE JUICES

For Healthy Living

BRIDGET JONES

CAXTON EDITIONS

CONTENTS

JUICE EXTRACTS

Refreshing and invigorating or relaxing and calming, fruit and vegetable juices provide a concentrated boost of benefits. The wealth of fruit and vegetables available in the shops or, increasingly, home-grown in even the smallest gardens, are a source of endless goodness.

One of the clear and unchanging messages that comes through the incredible volume of advice and information on healthy eating is that fruit and vegetables are good for us, and we should be eating more of them. Health experts recommend that we eat five portions of fruit and vegetables a day. That may sound a lot if your diet tends to be meat-based, with vegetables serving only as accompaniments (... it's time to change!), but it is not really. There are lots of ways of eating plenty of fruit and vegetables: try a portion of fruit for breakfast and as a snack during the day; include three decent-sized portions of vegetables with the main meal (frequently as main ingredients, not just accompaniments); include a reasonable portion of vegetables in a packed lunch or for a light meal (peppers, tomatoes and watercress taste wonderful in sandwiches); and have fruit as a dessert.

One of the best ways of boosting your fruit and vegetable intake is to include them in drinks. When juiced or puréed, vegetables and fruit are reduced to thirst-quenching drinks that provide all the vitamin goodness of a freshly prepared salad. Drink them as accompaniments or snacks and as an alternative to coffee or tea mid-morning or afternoon. Start and finish your day with juice – have a glass of energizing juice with breakfast; pour a refreshing welcome-home juice to wash away the worries of the working day; then try a soothing juice nightcap instead of a heavy milk drink.

Juices fit into all sorts of lifestyles and they may even change your lifestyle with their boost to the system and the spirit. There is certainly plenty of evidence that juices will boost the nutrient intake, providing vitamins, minerals and plant chemicals to do the body the world of good. As part of a healthy diet they will help in all sorts of ways – to keep the digestive system in order, fight infection and disease, make skin and hair look good, and extract maximum energy from other foods.

Drinking juices really does make you feel good and it is not just about nutrients. The feel-good factor is terrific – just shopping or picking all that fresh produce brings a virtuous glow of satisfaction. Making juices is hassle-free, with the minimum of trimming, cutting and chopping. There is no need to twitch about the type of knife or the look of the cuts; just hack, whizz and pour.

Remember that juices make a valuable contribution to a healthy diet, but they cannot compensate for a hopeless lack of attention to well-balanced eating. There is nothing wrong with the occasional indulgence – it often work wonders – but living on junk food, then trying to dose up on juice is not a good idea. Juices add food value to the diet, but they should not be used as meal replacements. A hearty juice with sustaining ingredients goes well with a simple carbohydrate breakfast or light lunch but it cannot replace a main meal.

Enjoy juicing and revel in the sense of well-being it brings.

There are complementary ingredients that can bring additional benefits to juice drinks – herbs, spices and flavouring ingredients. And juices do not have to mean drinks: they can be transformed into soups, sauces or simple sweet dishes with the minimum of fuss. Use fresh juices in cooking for maximum food value. The information and ideas in the chapters that follow are intended to inspire you to experiment with different types of juice. There is also some background information on why it is a good idea in terms of nutrition, and thoughts on the influence of juice in the far broader context of well-being.

To state that food is the essential fuel on which our bodies rely seems a complete waste of words because it is fundamental: to eat to live is natural. In practice we have long outgrown this approach and there is an incredible number of reasons for eating and variety of foods or products to suit all sorts of occasions. Our diets can be as individual as our lifestyles and just as susceptible to fashion whims.

We Are What We Eat

The way we eat is entirely down to us and, ultimately, we are what we eat. The direct link between diet and our physical 'shape' is clear and there is also greater awareness of the influence food has on health in a wider sense. We realize that the way we feel is affected by diet – in the simplest sense, if we are physically fit and 'on form', then we tend to feel good. In a different context, the foods we eat also affect our attitude and state of mind. This is widely appreciated in some ways; for example, we talk about 'comfort' foods or 'heart-warming' soups as the types of dishes that lift the spirits or make us feel secure when we are feeling vulnerable. As well as the aesthetics of eating and associations with mood, the components of food can act as stimulants or relaxants, to enliven or calm our minds and bodies.

Good Eating is Good News

There is no such thing as a 'bad' food. In this context, I refer to natural plant or animal foods and not products manufactured from basic ingredients that we would not recognize as being potentially edible. Excluding some types of food on a whim that they may be 'unhealthy' is neither sensible nor beneficial. This is particularly true when the condemned item is enjoyable or makes other foods palatable, so that cutting it out completely leads only to cravings and occasional bingeing or a diet that is dull. Avoiding complete categories of food for no good reason can also result in deficiencies because valuable nutrients are excluded. There is no great secret to good eating – it is all about variety and balance.

A Positive Approach to Balanced Eating

If the concept of healthy eating was nudged aside because it took on a brown and wholemeal image, balanced eating has almost acquired a reputation for being a damping-down regime – never too much of a good thing! However, being dull is precisely what a balanced diet avoids.

The first interpretation of balanced diet – and ultimately the most important – is enjoyable, long-term eating. The second is variety. Eating lots of different types of food provides a good range of nutrients; at the same time, individual foods are less likely to be eaten in unhealthily large quantities. Balancing a diet means eating different foods in the proportions the body needs them.

The Right Proportions

Starchy carbohydrates – foods like bread, potatoes, pasta, rice and other grains – are the best source of energy for the body. They are satisfying and the right type of food to fill you up. Fruit and vegetables are vital for vitamins and minerals as well as other benefits that are just being investigated by scientists; they should be eaten in generous quantities daily. Proteins are essential for growth and repair of the body, but they are not needed in as large a proportion. Animal sources of protein – including fish, poultry and meat – should be balanced by vegetable proteins, such as beans and pulses. Fats are important in the diet, but only in modest proportions, so foods that are high in fat should not be eaten regularly in large quantities. Animal fats, in particular, should be limited.

The human body is a sophisticated machine that uses food in a complex way; although it is possible to classify the roles of different nutrients, in practice their functions are interwoven. Even so, appreciating the characteristics of different types of food and their key nutrients highlights the need for a balanced diet and what it really means.

Carbohydrates

These are starches (complex carbohydrates) and sugars (simple carbohydrates). They are the satisfying foods and the energy providers. Starchy foods should form the base for a healthy diet. Energy is released slowly from complex carbohydrates, so not only do they feel filling when first eaten but they also provide a steady source of energy for some time.

Eating starches that are unrefined and high in fibre is also important – white flour and bread are fine, but it is a good idea to eat some wholemeal bread too. Breakfast cereals and whole grains are also valuable. Fibre is carbohydrate that the body cannot digest and break down completely, so it is passed out of the body. It absorbs liquid to provide bulk and moisture for the waste products of digestion allowing them to be excreted easily and preventing constipation. There are different types of fibre, some from fruit and vegetables and others from starchy carbohydrates. We need a good mixture of different types, including soluble fibre from oats and the pectin content of fruit, believed to help to moderate cholesterol levels.

Sugars occur naturally in some vegetables (particularly beetroot) and many fruits. Naturally sweet foods make good sweeteners instead of using pure sugar. There is nothing wrong with sugar, but it becomes a problem food when it is eaten to excess as it provides 'empty' calories. Eating lots of sugary snacks can result in a weight problem. More importantly, high-sugar snacks and sweet, acidic fruit drinks cause dental caries, particularly in children and young people. It is easy to acquire a 'sweet tooth' or taste for confectionery and very sweet drinks but equally easy to avoid this by encouraging young children to drink diluted juices that are low in sugar and healthy snacks, such as raw fruit and vegetables. Reserving sugary confectionery for occasional treats, rather than regular snacks, is important.

Proteins

Fish, poultry and meat are the main animal protein foods; dairy produce, such as eggs, cheese and milk, is also a source. Proteins are made up of amino acids. There are 7 essential amino acids that the body needs from food and animal protein provides all of them. Plant foods also provide protein, but they do not include all the essential amino acids in any one food. Soya beans are the exception and they are a source of high-quality protein. Other beans and pulses, rice and grains also provide protein. When a good mixture of vegetable foods is eaten the body obtains all the amino acids it needs.

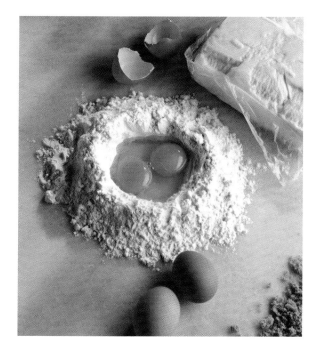

Fats

Fatty acids, obtained from fat, are essential in the diet. Fats are known as saturated or unsaturated, according to their chemical composition. The unsaturated fats may be polyunsaturated or monounsaturated. Animal fats tend to have a higher content of saturated fat than vegetable fats (although there are exceptions to this: coconut has a high saturated fat content). The amount of fat in the diet should be limited to a small amount daily and the majority of the fat we eat should be unsaturated. High-fat foods, such as butter, cheese, cream, fatty meats, oils and oil-based spreads and dressings, should be used only in modest amounts.

Vitamins

Vitamins occur in a wide range of foods and they are important for numerous general or specific functions. They are the catalysts in many situations, sparking off processes and/or ensuring they work successfully. They also help to protect the body against infection and damage, maintaining general good health as well as protecting against disease.

Vitamins are grouped into water-soluble types – vitamins C and B group – and fat-soluble types – vitamins A, D, E and K.

Water-soluble vitamins are not stored in the body for any length of time but the excess is excreted, so the body needs regular supplies. These vitamins seep out of food into cooking liquids. They are sensitive to heat and light, and the levels in food diminish with staleness.

Fat-soluble vitamins are stored in the body – they are still required regularly, but they can be eaten to excess. These are not as easily lost during food preparation and boiling, but they are lost with fat during roasting, frying and grilling.

The Water-soluble Vitamins

Vitamin C is found in fruit and vegetables. It is vital for healthy tissue throughout the body and known as the important vitamin for good skin. It plays a role in assisting the body to absorb and utilize other nutrients, such as iron. Vitamin C is also an antioxidant, helping to protect the body and repair damage caused by free radicals.

The B-group Vitamins This group of vitamins is important for the metabolism – or breaking down, absorption and use – of food. They each contribute to other vital functions, including maintaining a healthy nervous system and generating red blood cells.

Vitamin B1 or thiamin is found in meat and offal, whole grains, nuts, beans and pulses. It is important for the nervous system and for ensuring that the body can release and use energy from food.

Vitamin B2 or riboflavin is found in meat, offal, eggs, milk and its products, fish and fortified cereals and flours. Riboflavin helps the body to release and use energy from food. Riboflavin is light sensitive – so the content in milk diminishes if it is left to stand in the sun.

Niacin or nicotinic acid is found in poultry, meat, fish, nuts and vegetables. It is essential for cell function and for passing messages through the nervous system. It is important for the release and use of energy.

Vitamin B6 or pyridoxine is found in many foods, including fish, poultry, meat, vegetables, cereals, nuts and yeast extract. It is important for the formation of red blood cells, for a healthy immune system and for breaking down protein.

Vitamin B12 or cobalamin is found in animal foods, including fish, poultry, meat, eggs and dairy produce. It is also found in fortified breakfast cereals. This vitamin is essential for producing DNA and therefore it is vital for all cell generation, including the formation of red blood cells. Since it is widely available in foods, deficiency is rare; however, those following a vegan diet, excluding all animal products, are vulnerable.

Folate or folic acid is found in green vegetables, liver, wheatgerm and fortified cereals. It is essential for the production of red blood cells and all DNA. It is particularly important before conception and during pregnancy for the development of the baby.

Pantothenic acid is found in most foods, including meat and offal, vegetables, dried fruit and nuts. It assists in the release of energy and the manufacture of red blood cells, cholesterol and fat.

The Fat-soluble Vitamins

Vitamin A or retinol is found in animal foods, such as liver, milk and its products, and eggs. Beta carotene, found in highly coloured fruit and vegetables, including carrots, red and orange peppers, mango, apricots and green leafy vegetables, is converted into vitamin A in the body. Vitamin A is important for night vision. It is also used in cell construction and for the mucous membranes in the eyes, respiratory and digestive tracts. It promotes healthy skin and general cell building.

Vitamin D is found in liver, oily fish, eggs and fortified margarines. It is also synthesized in the body from exposure to sunlight. Deficiency is rare, except in those who are confined indoors, such as some elderly people. Vitamin D is important for calcium and phosphorus absorption, therefore for healthy bones and teeth.

Vitamin E is found in vegetable fats and oils, including nuts and seeds, oils and avocados. Vitamin E is an important antioxidant, protecting the body from damage caused by free radicals.

Vitamin K is found in green leafy vegetables. It is important for normal clotting of the blood.

KNOWING THE NUTRIENTS

Minerals

A range of minerals is required for assisting with specific and general functions throughout the body. The levels of some minerals in plant foods depend on their levels in the soil, so these vary from region to region. The fact that some minerals are required in small amounts does not diminish their importance and the need to ensure an adequate supply.

Calcium is found in milk and milk products, sardines and other fish when the bones are also eaten (such as canned salmon), shellfish, dark leafy green vegetables and sesame seeds. Oxalic acid in spinach and phytic acid in the outer layers of whole grains inhibit the absorption of calcium. Vitamin D is also essential for calcium absorption. Calcium is important for healthy bones and teeth.

Copper is found in a wide range of foods and deficiency is rare. Liver, shellfish, nuts and mushrooms all provide copper. It helps the body to absorb iron from food and to make red blood cells. It is also important in the manufacture of connective tissue and it helps to protect against damage from free radicals.

Fluorine is found in water to varying degrees, depending on soil and local policies on fluoridation of tap water, and in tea. It is important for maintaining the enamel coating on teeth and for healthy bones, but an excess can be damaging, causing over-formation or hardening of bones.

Iodine is found in seafood, including seaweed, vegetables and fruit. The levels of iodine in food depend on the soil, with more in coastal areas. Iodine is essential in small amounts for the functioning of the thyroid gland and the levels of hormone it produces, part of whose function is control of energy production as well as growth and development. Iodine deficiency leads to an under-active thyroid gland and one of the symptoms is a general lack of energy.

Iron is found in meat and offal, egg yolks and green leafy vegetables. The high levels of iron in vegetables such as spinach and watercress are not as easily absorbed as the iron in animal sources. Vitamin C helps the body to absorb iron, so combining foods rich in this vitamin with those rich in iron is beneficial. The body limits the amount of iron that can be absorbed and stored, so a regular supply is essential. Iron is best known for its role in haemoglobin or red blood cells, but it is also important for the proper functioning of enzymes.

Phosphorus is found in animal foods, plants and whole grains, and deficiency is rare. It is vital for healthy bones and teeth, and for energy production. It is also found in, and important to the function of, body proteins. Since it is so widely available, it is rarely deficient but it can be eaten in too large a quantity. The quantities of phosphorus and calcium in the diet should be balanced – if there is too much phosphorus, the body can reduce its calcium absorption, resulting in calcium deficiency. There is unlikely to be a problem with a diet that is rich in natural foods as phosphorus and calcium are found in the same foods. However, phosphorus is also found in processed foods in the form of phosphates (compounds of phosphorus), and diets with a high content of processed foods, rich in phosphates but low in calcium, can lead to an imbalance.

Potassium is found in most foods, especially meat, whole grains, vegetables, celery, citrus fruit and bananas. Along with sodium, potassium is important for fluid balance in the body and for efficient nerve and muscle activity.

Selenium is widely found in food, but the levels depend on those in the soil. Fish, meat, offal, dairy produce, citrus fruit, grains and avocados are good sources. Selenium plays many roles in proper hormone activity, growth and development. It is important for good eyesight and healthy hair and, as an antioxidant, it helps to protect against damage from free radicals.

Sodium is found in sodium chloride or salt. Sodium is essential, along with potassium, for balancing fluid levels in the body. It is also essential for nerve and muscle function. Salt is so widely used in food products and as a

Magnesium is found in dairy produce, grains, pulses, green vegetables and nuts as well as in many other foods. Deficiency is rare when a good mixed diet is eaten. Magnesium is important for enzyme activity and the function of the nervous system as well as muscles.

Manganese is found in plant foods in levels that depend on the amount in the soil. It is available from whole grains and their products, pulses and nuts. It plays many roles, especially in enzyme activity, and is important for proper thyroid function, insulin production, muscle and nerve function. Deficiency is rare in a healthy mixed diet because manganese is widely available in food.

Molybdenum is widely distributed in plant foods and liver, and deficiency is rare. It has many roles as it is important for the proper functioning of enzymes.

seasoning that the problem is not one of deficiency but of diets with too high a sodium content. Sodium is essential in the diet and it is lost in sweat, so levels have to be replenished. However, processed foods and prepared products often have a very high salt content, so when they are eaten regularly they can create an excess in the body. Diets with a very high salt content contribute to high blood pressure.

Sulphur is found in animal foods and vegetable proteins, such as pulses, as it is a compound found in proteins. Sulphur is an important mineral in body proteins, including skin, hair, nails and connective tissue. It is also found in hormones, so vital to many functions in the body.

Zinc is found in all animal foods, particularly fish and shellfish, and also in whole grains. The zinc in animal foods is more readily available to the body than that in vegetable sources. It is important for enzyme activity and a wide range of functions, including the activities of the immune system, night vision, taste and digestion, and energy production.

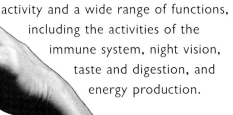

Plant-Food Potential

The value of fruit and vegetables in the diet is a comparatively recent discovery. Health experts recommend that five portions of fruit and vegetables should be eaten daily. A diet rich in plant foods, with plenty of starch, a good fibre content, modest amounts of protein, a little fat, and based on light cooking methods seems to help in the fight against disease. Plant foods in particular play a valuable protective role. The importance of vitamins, minerals and fibre is well established; the extent of the contribution from other components found in plant foods is only just being discovered.

Phytochemicals

In addition to the well-documented nutrients, the many thousand other substances that make up edible plants contribute to health. Many plant chemicals or phytochemicals are thought to protect the body against disease and its causes, particularly against free radicals which latch on to cells in the body or oxidize them. The protection offered by including plenty of fruit, vegetables and other plant foods in the diet is thought to be helpful in preventing cancer among other diseases. This is a comparatively new and developing area – scientists are just beginning to discover and further explore the potential of plant foods. The following are some of the benefits being discussed and outlined by nutritionists to date.

Carotenes or carotenoids are well known, particularly beta carotene, the substance that gives carrots and other vegetables and fruit strong colour. Lycopene is the carotenoid in tomatoes and it is believed to help reduce the risk of prostate cancer.

⬤ Allicin is another substance that occurs in vegetables with well-established use in herbal medicine. It is found in plants of the onion family, including all types of onions, leeks and garlic. These plants, and garlic in particular, are thought to help to lower blood pressure and therefore help to prevent heart disease; they are also believed to help reduce high blood cholesterol levels.

⬤ Glucosolinates are found in the Crucifera family of vegetables, which includes mustard greens, cabbage, curly kale, Brussels sprouts, broccoli, cauliflower, swedes (rutabagas) and radishes. The glucosolinates include a vast group of substances believed to help protect against cancer. The glucosolinates help to speed up the rate at which potentially damaging substances are processed and excreted from the body. Sulphoraphane is one of these substances believed to be particularly beneficial.

⬤ Flavonoids or bio-flavonoids are found in flowers and tree bark as well as in fruit and vegetables. There are many sub-groups of flavonoids, including flavonols, and isoflavones, depending on their exact chemical structure, and there are thousands of different substances in these groups. They are antioxidants and protect against disease. The flavonoids are often associated with vegetables with a slightly sweet flavour because they contain glucose compounds. Anthocyanins are flavonoids responsible for the red, violet and blue colours in the skin of many fruits, such as berries.

⬤ Phytoestrogens are plant chemicals that are similar to oestrogen, the female sex hormone, and their activity is similar to the hormone. They include substances found in a variety of plant foods; isoflavones (a sub-group of flavonoids) are phytoestrogens that may help counteract menopausal problems.

Free Radicals

Free radicals are oxygen particles that are a by-product of normal metabolism. They are also produced in response to infection, some chemicals and environmental forces, such as exposure to ultra-violet light (in sunlight). They are highly reactive and damage the cells in the body, in turn causing damage to DNA. The damage caused by free radicals is linked with diseases such as cancer, athero-sclerosis (where there is a build-up of material in the arteries, restricting blood flow) and heart disease. The antioxidant nutrients are important for neutralizing free radicals or repairing the damage they cause.

FABULOUS FRUIT

Fruit needs no introduction as a source of refreshing juice, but it is easy to focus on the familiar and forget about the cornucopia of produce available for making exciting and nutritious drinks. Fruit is a valuable source of vitamins, particularly vitamin C, and fibre. Fruit is also useful to varying degrees as a laxative and helpful in preventing constipation. From the old saying that 'an apple a day keeps the doctor away' to the comparatively recent enthusiasm for the protective benefits of plant chemicals from fruit in preventing cancer and other diseases, fruit has a long-established reputation as a full-of-goodness food.

Packing the diet full of fruit is a pleasure as it is good to eat. One of the best ways of increasing the amount of fruit is to include regular fruit juice drinks: with breakfast, as accompaniments to main meals, as appetizers,

for a snack or as a nightcap instead of heavy dairy drinks. Fruit juices also make good desserts – in sorbets and ice creams, as lightly sweetened fruit soups or in jellies and creams.

Virtually any fruit can be used alone, with other fruit or with vegetables. Frozen fruit is just as good as fresh fruit and a practical choice for winter. Juicing or puréeing home-grown fruit and freezing it in small tubs is also a good way of preserving a glut for later use. Make the most of apples, oranges and other less expensive fruit to extend exotic fruit or berries. It is also worth noting that frozen berries (raspberries, for example) are often cheaper than the fresh fruit; they may even have a better flavour and more food value as they are picked at their prime and frozen promptly after harvesting, so preserving their optimum vitamin C content.

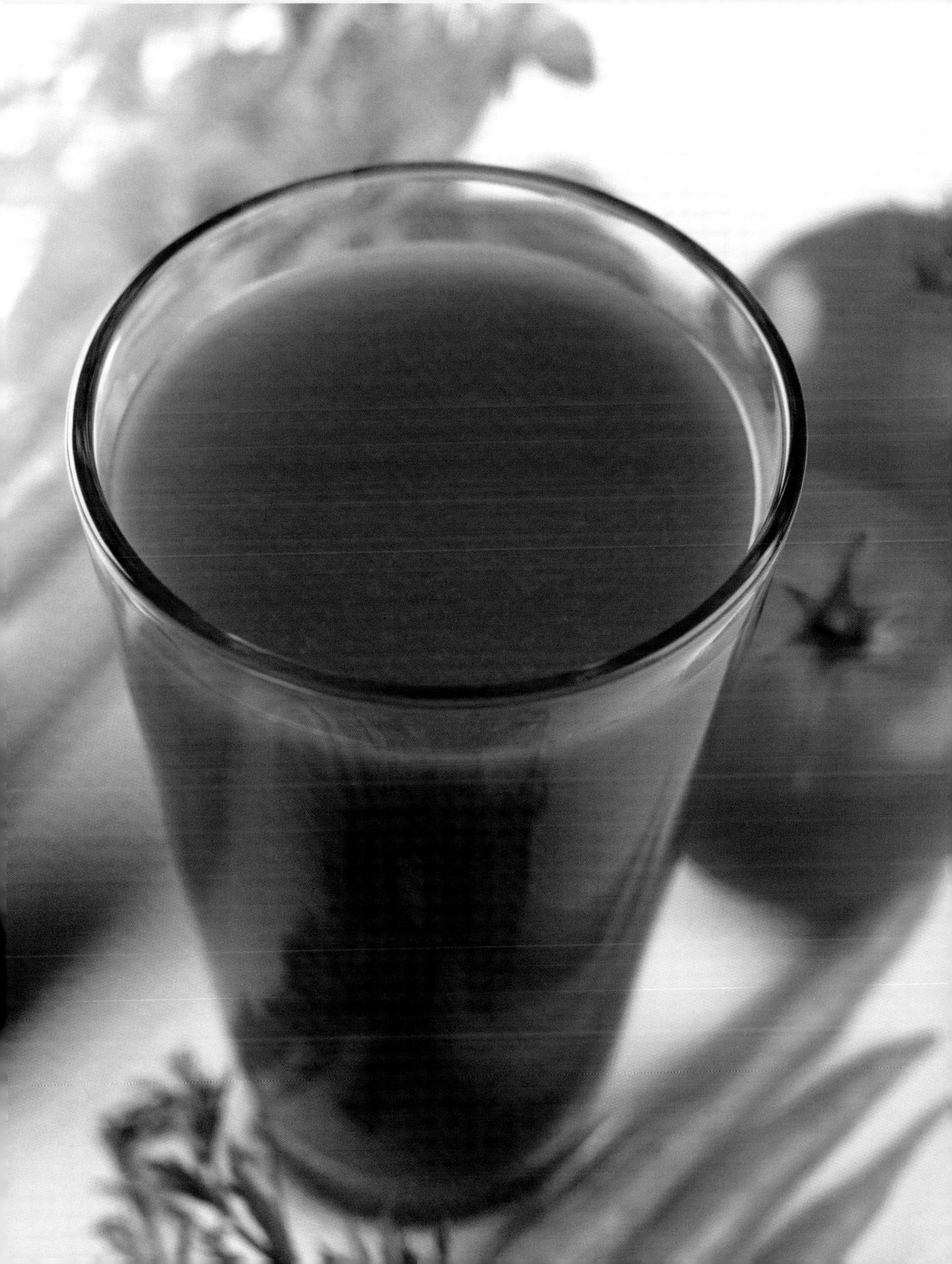

Apples

Current enthusiasm for the health benefits of apples comes as much from their pectin content and plant chemical goodness as from the vitamin C they provide. Pectin is a soluble fibre, believed to help control cholesterol levels. Along with other fruit, apples are appreciated for their antioxidant value. There are many types of dessert apple, with flavours varying from delicate and scented to robust, sweet and very fruity, and all are excellent for juicing and making drinks.

Apricots

Apricots are a good source of beta carotene, vitamin C and fibre. They make a rich and full-flavoured juice that is smooth and luscious. It can be combined with other fruit juices, such as orange or apple, or with carrot juice.

Bananas

Bananas are satisfying and they provide fibre. As they ripen, their starch content changes to sugar. They are a good source of potassium and they provide some vitamin C along with some vitamin B6 or pyridoxine and vitamin E. They do not provide a 'juice' as such, but are terrific when puréed with liquids, for example with milk or yogurt, or with other fruit juices.

Berries

The berries include blueberries, blackberries, strawberries and raspberries. These are good sources of anthocyanins, plant chemicals known as flavonoids, that are valuable antioxidants and useful anti-bacterial agents. They also provide vitamins C and E, and fibre, including pectin, appreciated as a valuable soluble fibre. Berries provide full-flavoured juice which can be extended by combining the berries with apples, pears, bananas or vegetables, such as carrots or beetroot. They go well with oats or yogurt in smoothies.

Cherries

Cherries provide vitamin C, potassium and fibre. They are thought of as a cleansing fruit and are said to help to relieve gout when eaten in significant quantities. They provide full-flavoured juice which combines well with that of other fruit and vegetable juices, particularly beetroot juice.

Citrus Fruit

Lemons, limes, oranges, grapefruit, satsumas and other familiar citrus fruit are all well known as ideal ingredients for juices and drinks. They provide vitamin C, valuable plant chemicals and fibre. Use the rind, pith and all the membranes whenever possible because these are full of goodness, particularly pectin and flavonoids. Lemon is traditionally thought of as a stimulant to the immune system, helpful as a cold cure, a tonic and a balancing ingredient promoting an alkaline state when neutralized during digestion. In aesthetic terms, orange has a sunny, warming influence and is helpful in encouraging sleep. So it is a useful ingredient for soothing nightcaps as well as for stimulating breakfast drinks.

Juiced or reduced to a purée, citrus is widely used with other fruit or vegetable juices. The sharp tang of lemon juice accentuates other flavours and citrus juice also helps to prevent fruit such as apples, pears and bananas from discolouring. The rind brings full flavour to fruit and vegetable juices, and it is particularly useful as a link between sweet and savoury ingredients, for example, in vegetable cocktails. Citrus fruits are coated with a fine wax to prevent moisture loss by evaporation, so they should be scrubbed before the rind is used.

Cranberries

Cranberries are very rich in vitamin C and pectin. Cranberry juice is recommended for helping to combat or prevent urinary tract infections. They are extremely bitter and quite seedy. They go well with pears, bananas and substantial fruit in smoothies sweetened with honey. They are also good with beetroot or carrot juices.

FABULOUS FRUIT

Currants

Blackcurrants and redcurrants are full-flavoured fruit that provide excellent juices or purées. Blackcurrants are a particularly rich source of vitamin C. Anthocyanins, plant chemicals known as flavonoids, give the berries their bright skins and they are useful antioxidants. These plant chemicals are also anti-bacterial and anti-inflammatory, so useful for helping to soothe sore throats. The strong flavours of currants go well with other fruits, carrots and beetroot.

Grapes

Grapes provide potassium and natural sweetening for a variety of juices. The skin of black and red grapes includes antioxidant plant chemicals which are thought to be beneficial in preventing cancer and heart disease. Grapes go well with vegetable and fruit juices, and are an excellent fruit for sweetening juices. Try them with papaya, apple, pear, cranberries, redcurrants, cucumber or fennel.

FABULOUS FRUIT

Guavas

Guava has a mild, scented and slightly exotic flavour. It is a fibrous fruit, therefore a useful source of fruit fibre, and it provides a good supply of vitamin C as well as potassium. Guava goes well with grapes and other lightly flavoured fruit. Try making a rich smoothie by combining guava and plain cashew nuts with yogurt; or mix it with lime to make a refreshing drink.

Kiwi Fruit

Kiwi fruit is rich in vitamin C – far more so than orange – and it also provides potassium and fibre. The flavour is excellent for a variety of juices as it goes well with apple, banana, lime, grapes or vegetables, including carrot, spinach, peppers or peas.

Lychees

Expensive but scented and distinct in flavour, lychees can be combined with other light fruit. For example, they bring flavour to pears, apples or green grapes. They are complemented by lime juice. Use them in smoothies, with yogurt or oats.

Mangoes

Bright mangoes provide beta carotene and vitamin C, so they are a good fruit for preventing damage from free radicals and for generally acting in a protective role. Sweet, smooth and rounded in flavour, slightly sharp when barely ripe, mangoes are versatile in juices with other fruit or vegetables. They go with almost anything – light juice, luscious yogurt or smoothies made with oats. Try mango with berries, orange, lime or banana for fabulous fruitiness; it is the perfect foil for carrot juice and lively with cucumber and celery; or mix it with red pepper and orange for a super boost of antioxidant nutrients.

Melons

Delicate melons vary according to type – the varieties with orange flesh provide beta carotene. In juices, their sweet and scented flavour is excellent with cucumber, fennel, apple and celery. They are good for bulking out peaches, nectarines, plums, guavas and other exotic fruit in drinks that pack two weeks of summer relaxation into one long glass! Try melons with buttermilk or yogurt, scented with mint and spiked with a little fresh root ginger.

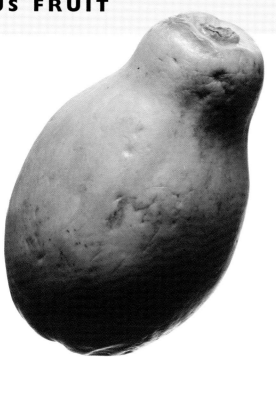

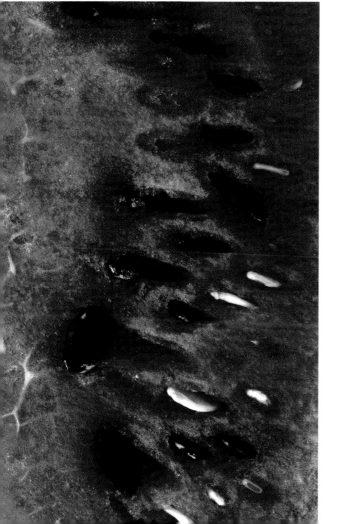

Papayas

Smooth and delicate papayas contain beta carotene and vitamin C. They aid digestion and are thought to be helpful in pain relief. Use papaya with apples, pears, bananas, carrots or oranges to bulk it out. Papaya is also excellent with avocado and mint in a creamy dessert or with tomato and cucumber for a cooling summer soup.

FABULOUS FRUIT

Passion Fruit

Fragrant and fanciful, passion fruit really lifts
the spirits. Remember to save the seeds and
add them as a crunchy topping – perhaps with
some chopped walnuts on a swirl of Greek-
style yogurt – on tall glasses of exotic juice.
Bring a bolt of summer flavour and goodness
to a dull winter's day by whizzing up frozen
blackcurrants and passion fruit juice into a
dark and mysterious drink. Top with yogurt
and crunchy seeds and make it an excuse for a
relaxing break.

FABULOUS FRUIT

Peaches and Nectarines

Peaches and nectarines provide vitamin C and fibre. They make smooth, luscious juice, which is sweet and rich from ripe fruit. Combine peaches with apples, pears, orange, grape or carrot. They are good in light juices, smoothies or creams.

Pears

Pears are a good source of fibre and also provide some vitamin C and potassium. They are a useful fruit for bulking out aromatic exotics, especially in smoothies. They are particularly easy on the digestive system, so an excellent choice for soothing smoothies. Try pear and oat smoothie as a tempting snack when the appetite is poor; combine pear and mango to make the most of the beta carotene in the mango; mix pear with pineapple, ginger and yogurt for an invigorating breakfast drink.

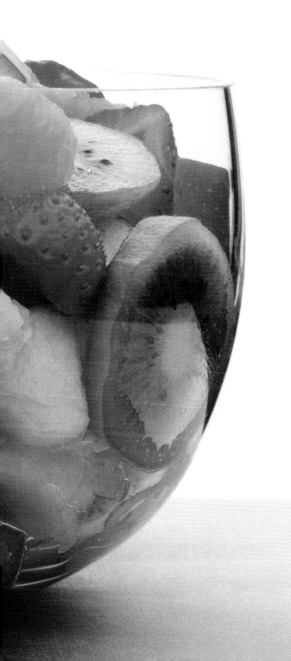

Pineapples

As a folk cure, pineapple was attributed with healing and soothing properties as well as a reputation for clearing the head, reducing catarrh and chest congestion. Fresh pineapple does contain an enzyme that is highly effective in breaking down protein (this is destroyed by canning and pasteurization).

FABULOUS FRUIT

Plums

Plums provide vitamins C and E, and potassium. Being a stone fruit, they can be tedious for juicing, especially the type from which the stones (pits) are not easily removed. They can be combined with bulky fruit, such as bananas, pears or apples, to use their full flavour to best advantage.

Pomegranates

Sweet and seedy, pomegranates produce a juice that is syrup-like and good with tangy fruit. The seeds are so crunchy and delicious that they make a fabulous contrasting topping for smoothies and slightly acidic fruit juices, fruit soups or fruit and vegetable soups.

Dried Fruit

Dried fruit is excellent for sweetening and enriching fresh fruit juices and drinks. It is also a useful source of fibre. Dried apricots provide iron and beta carotene. Prunes, peaches and apricots are especially good with citrus juice, carrots, apples, pears or light vegetables, such as fennel, celery or cucumber in combination with citrus fruit. They provide energy in breakfast drinks and help to prevent constipation.

VEGETABLE VARIETY

VEGETABLE VARIETY

*O*f you are comparatively new to juice-making at home, it is worth remembering that some vegetable juices can be an acquired taste. It is not necessarily a good thing to launch straight into a healthy drinks campaign by preparing a morning concoction of broccoli, spinach, garlic and green pepper, for example. It may provide a mega-boost to your nutrient intake, but having to hold your nose to down the drink is hardly likely to encourage a long-term sense of enjoyment and well-being. Do not let preconceived ideas on colour and ingredient combinations stop you from experimenting, but do mix small amounts at first.

The chances are you will be delighted by the amazing flavours that result from combining vegetables with fruit in light or substantial drinks. My first forays into drink-making with leafy green vegetable juices were taken with tip-toe care but I was soon leaping about with enthusiasm and confidence. Sweet and juicy apples, grapes, kiwi and pineapple were delicious with their fresh green flavours. Tangy citrus, fresh-tasting fennel, earthy ginseng, spicy ginger and super-fruity berries tasted fantastic with carrot juice – something I had always found to be rather too dominant in drinks before (although I love carrots in cooking, especially in soups). Discovering vegetables in a new context is exciting and the drinks bring a glorious sense of well-being just from their flavours quite apart from the unquestionable nutritional boost they provide.

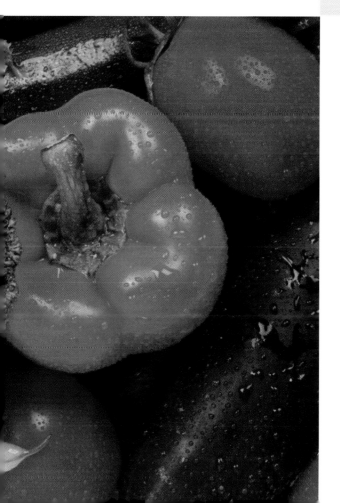

Vegetables with a high moisture content yield useful quantities of juice; starchy root vegetables, such as parsnips and potatoes, are not practical. The following are the main vegetables for juicing and puréeing, but it is worth experimenting with others, especially for making soups.

VEGETABLE VARIETY

Asparagus

Asparagus provides vitamins C and E, folate and beta carotene. It is also a diuretic. Asparagus contains sulphur compounds that make urine smell strongly. Gout sufferers should be aware that asparagus contains purines that can encourage a build up of uric acid which aggravates the condition. Juicing or puréeing and straining asparagus provides a rich source of the nutrients and fabulous flavour. Save the cooking water from asparagus for vegetable and herb drinks. Asparagus, lemon and cucumber go together well; or try asparagus and apple with lemon juice.

Avocado

Avocado provides vitamins C and B6, and riboflavin as well as copper and some iron. It is unusual for its comparatively high protein and fat contents (largely polyunsaturated) and as a good source of vitamin E. Avocado tastes terrific with vegetable or fruit juices in cold soups or for making savoury cocktails with a creamy texture.

Beetroot

Bright, slightly earthy and sweet, beetroot provides rich, full-flavoured juice. Beetroot provides folate, potassium and vitamin C. It is reputed to help to prevent cancer. Beetroot juice has an established reputation as an excellent tonic. Beetroot can be juiced either raw or cooked; using a juicer is the best way of processing the raw vegetable, while cooked can be juiced or puréed. Beetroot goes wonderfully well with fruity berries, such as raspberries, or with citrus flavours. Its sweet flavour is also complemented by tangy yogurt in smoothies and slightly creamy soups.

Cabbage Family

Along with the many types of cabbage and Brussels sprouts, broccoli and cauliflower are part of this brassica family of cruciferous vegetables. They provide vitamins C, E, K and thiamin; folate; beta carotene; and potassium. These are particularly valuable for the phytochemicals they contain, thought to help protect against cancer. Although cabbages and Brussels sprouts may not have immediate appeal for their juice value, broccoli and cauliflower go well with carrots and tomatoes in light vegetable cocktails and soups. Both red and white cabbage are good with more powerful mixtures, especially in soups.

VEGETABLE VARIETY

Carrots

Beta carotene gives carrots their characteristic colour. They are an excellent ingredient for juicing: inexpensive and juicy, with a mild, sweet flavour, they are ideal for adding bulk to the more expensive ingredients, such as exotic fruit. They taste terrific with oranges, apples, exotic fruit, peppers, ginseng, herbs and spices in cool or hot long drinks or cocktails. They go well in savoury or sweet concoctions, drinks, sauces or soups. They juice well or they can be puréed and served thick or strained. Raw carrots provide the fresh flavour required for drinks, but cooked carrots are equally valuable for soups. Cooking carrots helps to make the beta carotene more accessible to the body and, as a purée, provides a good base for raw fruit juices in simple soups.

Celery

Celery provides potassium and is one of the foods that may help to reduce blood pressure; it is also thought to be beneficial for those suffering from gout. Traditionally, celery has a reputation for its calming and sedative effects, as a diuretic and a general tonic. It goes well with citrus flavours, apples; pears and juices; in savoury cocktails and soups; and with most vegetables, particularly tomatoes, cucumber and carrots.

Zucchini

The skin provides folate and beta carotene and courgettes also provide fibre. They are useful for diluting the flavour of strong fruit and vegetables, providing inexpensive bulk for more costly ingredients. Try courgettes with citrus, mango, passion fruit, kiwi, cucumber, tomatoes, peppers or broccoli.

Cucumber

Cucumber is wonderfully refreshing and it acts as a mild diuretic. Cucumber is cooling and has calming associations with cosmetics and pampering. It combines well with fruit or vegetables – use it to extend strawberries, raspberries and other berries; combine it with lemon, apple and orange; mix it with peppers and tomatoes; or blend it with strong cauliflower or broccoli. Cucumber is especially good with yogurt and with eucalyptus-tinged spices, such as cardamom, or 'hot' ingredients, like ginger.

VEGETABLE VARIETY

Peas

Fresh or frozen peas provide some vegetable protein; vitamins B1 (thiamin) and B6; vitamin C and folate as well as beta carotene, phosphorus and fibre. Sugarsnap peas are particularly sweet and delicious for juices – one of the best ways of using them is to add them to a small quantity of boiling water (barely enough to cover the pods) and bring rapidly back to the boil in as few seconds as possible. Then drain immediately, saving the liquid, and rinse under cold water. Leave the cooking liquor to cool, then add it to the pods when juicing or puréeing. The idea is simply to take the raw edge off the flavour rather than to cook the vegetables. Combine pea juice with cucumber, celery and carrot; it goes well with apple and lime; or mix it with fennel and orange.

Onions

Onions have a homely reputation for being beneficial. Plants of this family (garlic, onions and leeks) have, in fact, long been recognized for their antiseptic, anti-fungal and anti-bacterial properties. These vegetables help to clear congestion associated with bad colds. Garlic, in particular, has been used for its medicinal properties for generations. The onion family has also acquired a reputation for helping to lower blood cholesterol levels, prevent clotting and protect against cancer.

VEGETABLE VARIETY

Peppers

Peppers are excellent sources of antioxidants: they are a super source of vitamin C (particularly red peppers) and provide beta carotene and flavonoids, natural plant chemicals. Green peppers have a fresh, slightly cutting and very 'green' flavour that complements apples, kiwi, lime, cucumber and grapes. Strangely, the red, orange and yellow peppers seem to go with fruits of those colours – try them with oranges, raspberries, redcurrants, mangoes or papayas.

VEGETABLE VARIETY

Spinach

Spinach is another vegetable renowned for its iron, but unfortunately it is bound by oxalic acid and largely unavailable to the body. Vitamin C from the spinach (and other sources) helps the body to absorb as much iron as possible. Spinach also provides folate. It goes well with other green vegetables for savoury cocktails and simple soups; it also tastes good with fruit and the fresh flavour of fennel.

Watercress

Watercress provides plenty of folate and carotene. It is also rich in iron, but in a form not readily available to the body. Combine watercress with ingredients rich in vitamin C so that the body can extract as much iron as possible. Try a green pepper, watercress and fennel cocktail, spiking the flavour with a little garlic and lime to make an appetite-arousing first course. Or mix it with carrot and orange for a simple summer soup.

Tomatoes

Tomatoes provide vitamins C and E. They also contain lycopene, a carotene which gives them their red colour, and it is thought to be helpful in preventing prostate cancer. Lycopene is more readily available to the body from canned and processed forms of tomato, such as tomato juice. Tomato juice is an ingredient for traditional drinks, including Bloody Mary, mixed with vodka. It goes well with citrus fruit in drinks and with vegetable juices for cocktails or soups.

Herbs and spices are used in cookery for their complementary flavours; many have ancient medicinal uses and long-established roles in home cures or comforts. The essential oils of many culinary ingredients are often used in aromatherapy, with great care and respect because they can be extremely powerful.

In their plant form – the way they are usually used in cookery – herbs and spices are mild and, unlike the essential oils extracted from them, their active substances are not concentrated in potentially harmful amounts. Using these seasonings regularly in cooking, and particularly in juices and drinks, can make a positive contribution to the sense of well-being. Herbs and spices bring an additional dimension to infusions and tisanes in hot or cold drinks. They also go wonderfully well with fresh juices from both fruit and vegetables. In a very simple sense, they can help to promote a sense of calm or to enliven and invigorate. When used regularly, their contribution can be positive, especially from herbs like parsley, dill or fennel that are often used in significant amounts.

Herbs

One of the general characteristics of herbs is that they often aid digestion. In small quantities, herbs (and spices) do not make any valuable contribution by way of nutrients, but they support the main foods that contribute to health in a well-balanced diet. Many of these ingredients are valuable in drinks for soothing or stimulating; for balancing; and supporting or counteracting the frantic pace of life.

Angelica

Known in cookery as a bright green candied stem most often used to decorate cakes and sweet dishes. It is a shame that candied angelica is set aside only for decoration as it goes very well with walnuts in cakes. Angelica has a fresh 'green' flavour. It grows easily, forming tall, hollow stems with large seed-forming flower heads. The freshly picked stem can be washed and simmered in water to make an infusion for flavouring fruit juices or teas. The infusion can be used to make a useful syrup for sweetening drinks, making ice creams or sorbets, or flavouring fresh fruit salads. The seeds and roots are used in herbal medicine and the seeds are used to flavour liqueurs. In herbal medicine, angelica is credited as a great curative. It is said to be a good tonic and stimulant, helpful in detoxification and cleansing, and for strengthening the immune system.

Basil

Aromatic basil is widely appreciated in cooking for its lively flavour. It was once regarded as a stimulant and uplifting herb, but it is now generally regarded as calming. It is thought to aid digestion and to help ease headaches, migraine, stress and nervous disorders. It certainly has an uplifting flavour and it brings a ray of sunshine to soups and savoury dishes; it is also used to flavour some sweet fruit dishes.

Bay

Widely used to flavour savoury recipes, bay contributes a subtle spicy warmth to sweet dishes, including milk puddings and syrups. Bay aids digestion and is traditionally thought to help to cure colds and influenza.

Borage

A traditional herb for flavouring summer drinks and salads, borage has an ancient reputation for lifting the spirits. It has diuretic and anti-inflammatory properties, and is said to soothe catarrh and bronchitis.

Camomile

There are several species of camomile and it is best known for making herb tea. It is known as a calming herb, suitable for aiding sleep, and for easing stomach upsets.

Chervil

A cleansing herb, chervil has a reputation for assisting with urinary and liver complaints. It is similar in flavour to, but lighter than, parsley.

Coriander (Cilantro)

The leaves are full-flavoured, quite 'savoury', with a powerful, cutting flavour and quite sharp or fresh 'green' aroma. The seeds are very different – mellow and warm in aroma and flavour. Coriander has a reputation for aiding digestion and easing flatulence. It is also thought to stimulate the appetite.

Dill

The feathery fronds of the herb have a slightly aniseed flavour. The seeds are used as a spice and they reflect the flavour of the herb but in a subtle and more mature sense. Dill is known for aiding digestion, soothing indigestion and flatulence, and helping sleep. It is an ingredient in gripe water, given to babies suffering from colic.

Elderflower

The fabulous aroma and sweet, flowery flavour of elderflower is wonderful in fruit drinks and sweet dishes. Elderflower is traditionally thought of as a cleansing agent, diuretic and gentle laxative. It helps to ease catarrh and is thought to help relieve colds.

Fennel

The plant that provides the herb and spice
differs from the vegetable in that it does
not form the swollen stem base, the fennel
bulb used as the vegetable and sometimes
referred to as Florence fennel. The herb
takes the form of feathery fronds and the
seeds are used as a spice. They both have a
pronounced aniseed flavour and are
popular for herb teas. The vegetable, herb
and spice share similar properties, with a
reputation for aiding digestion and calming
the system. Fennel is said to ease nausea,
flatulence and indigestion. It is also a
diuretic.

Lavender

Lavender is used to flavour some desserts
and ices. Its distinctive aroma and flavour
complement sweet and fruity dishes.
Lavender has many uses, including
antiseptic and anti-bacterial; it is
appreciated for soothing colds, clearing the
head and easing catarrh. Its calming and
balancing properties are useful for helping
relaxation and aiding sleep.

Marjoram and Oregano

These are warming herbs, with marjoram being the milder and oregano (or wild marjoram as it is sometimes known) being stronger in flavour and properties. Marjoram and oregano are known for their antiseptic properties, useful in aiding treatment of sore throats. These are calming and sleep-inducing herbs, with warming and comforting properties that ease stress and distress.

Mint

There are many varieties of this familiar herb. Mint has a lively aroma and flavour, and it is a popular flavouring in sweet and savoury dishes and drinks. Mint is thought to aid digestion, calm the stomach, ease flatulence and assist in treating constipation. It has a reputation for being both soothing and stimulating.

Parsley

Parsley is a cleansing herb, with a reputation for neutralizing strong smells. It is a mild diuretic and thought to help regulate the menstrual cycle. It aids digestion and relieves flatulence.

Rosemary

Full-flavoured rosemary is widely used in savoury cookery and excellent for making herb tea. It has a reputation as an antiseptic. The flavour and aroma is warm and rosemary oil is thought to stimulate the nervous system and brain. It is a head-clearing herb, for easing headaches as well as helping with the congestion associated with colds. It is also thought to be a general tonic and may even help with lowering cholesterol levels.

Sage

Warm, peppery sage is widely used in savoury cooking. Its very familiarity is comforting. Traditionally, sage is thought of as a tonic and a healing herb. It is considered to be useful for calming nerves as well as stimulating the nervous system. It is said to promote good circulation. It was also used traditionally to stimulate menstruation.

Tarragon

Tarragon is a tender, fresh-tasting herb with a strong aniseed flavour (French tarragon is the herb cultivated for culinary use; Russian tarragon has little flavour). Tarragon is known as an aid to digestion, for easing flatulence and nausea. It has also been used to soothe toothache. Tarragon is a useful herb for tisanes and infusions to flavour fruit drinks; it is also excellent in vegetable juices for simple savoury soups and cocktails.

Thyme

Strongly aromatic and with a warm flavour, thyme is widely used in savoury cooking. It has a reputation as an antiseptic, helpful in the treatment of sore throats and mouth infections. Thyme is also said to stimulate the appetite and aid digestion. Thyme is another of the herbs that is thought to have a balancing effect – on the one hand it is stimulating, but it can also help to calm stress and therefore assist with sleep and relaxation

Spices

Spices from all over the world are now readily available in the majority of supermarkets. Spices are needed in quite small quantities in juices because the uncooked fruit and vegetables are not bulky and absorbing. Spices are usually more potent than their related herbs, both in flavour and in benefits, because they are mostly derived from the seeds or other parts of the plant that contain a higher concentration of essential plant substances. The benefits of spiced and herbal drinks are not from a one-off cup, but from including them in the diet on a fairly regular basis, for example, as regular alternatives to some – if not all – caffeine-rich drinks or alcohol. Like herbs, spices are traditional aids to digestion and are known particularly for relieving or helping to prevent flatulence, for example, when combined with pulses. Lightly spiced fruit and yogurt drinks make good accompaniments for high-fibre meals, including breakfast as well as the main meal of the day.

Aniseed

Aniseed has a strong flavour, appreciated in baking in European cookery and as one of the ingredients in Chinese five-spice powder. It is also used to flavour drinks and liqueurs, such as Greek ouzo and French Pernod. It has a reputation for stimulating the appetite, aiding digestion and relieving flatulence. It was also used as a traditional comfort for coughs, colds and asthma, and in soothing potions for helping sleep.

Caraway

Caraway seeds have a warm flavour that goes well with all sorts of fruit, especially in warm drinks. Caraway is warming and comforting, related to dill and fennel. It stimulates the appetite, aids digestion and relieves flatulence.

Cardamoms

Aromatic, refreshing and head-clearing, cardamoms are reminiscent of citrus and eucalyptus. They are said to aid digestion and settle the stomach as well as refresh the breath. Cardamoms make a soothing drink for those suffering from colds and influenza.

Cinnamon

Warming cinnamon helps to clear the head, so it is a helpful spice to include in cold-cure drinks. It is also believed to help aid digestion, relieve flatulence and promote circulation.

Cloves

Cloves have an affinity with apples and are a classic spice for making warming, mulled drinks – just as good with apple, pear or grape juice as with wine. Best-known as a home-cure for toothache, cloves possess anaesthetic and antiseptic qualities. Cloves are a stimulant and an aid to digestion and the relief of flatulence.

Coriander

Like the herb, coriander seeds are thought of as a stimulant and an aid to digestion. Although they are not widely used in drinks, the seeds go well with dried fruits, such as prunes, nuts and citrus flavours.

Cumin

Said to stimulate the appetite, cumin is not widely used in fruit drinks, but it goes well with vegetable juices, yogurt, citrus flavours and mint. It is a diuretic and a stimulant.

Dill

Dill seeds are the spice from the dill plant.
See Herbs.

Fennel

Fennel seeds are the spice from the fennel
plant. See Herbs.

Ginger

Ginger is available as the fresh root;
preserved in syrup or candied; as the dried
root; or dried and ground to a powder.
Fresh root ginger tastes terrific with a wide
variety of vegetable and fruit juices in drinks,
soups and all sorts of dishes. Ginger is
known for easing nausea and diarrhoea. It is
said to promote sweating and improve
circulation as well as to help fight against
infection as a cold-cure drink.

Juniper

Little dark berries – almost black – used
for bringing a rich flavour to game, poultry
and meat in cooking, juniper is also a good
spice for enriching mulled and warm
drinks. It is one of the flavouring
ingredients in gin. Known as a diuretic and
antiseptic, juniper is a cleansing spice, used
to promote detoxication and as a tonic. It
is also an appetite stimulant.

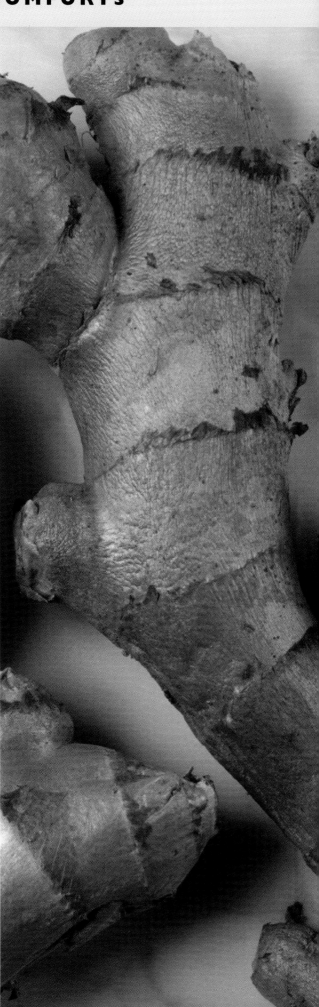

Mustard

Mustard is warming, known for traditional use in poultices and hot mustard baths. It goes well with tomato juice and mixtures of vegetable juices to make warming drinks and soups that are comforters to soothe the symptoms of colds.

Nutmeg and Mace

Warm spices that aid digestion, and act as a stimulant and a tonic. They can ease nausea and flatulence. In large quantities, these spices can cause drowsiness and hallucinations, and can even be poisonous, but in the amounts used in cookery, there is no danger.

Turmeric

Bright yellow in colour, with an earthy, yet refreshing, flavour, turmeric has a reputation as a tonic, stimulant and anti-bacterial and anti-septic spice.

OTHER BENEFICIAL INGREDIENTS

ruit and vegetables may be the main ingredients in juices, but a variety of other beneficial foods are often added to alter the image of the juice, making simple soups or desserts as well as a variety of different drinks. The following are a few examples – you will probably combine the juices with a broader spectrum of delicious foods once you are using them to their full potential.

Garlic

Garlic is believed to assist in lowering blood cholesterol levels and to help in the treatment of high blood pressure and heart disease. It is also antiseptic and detoxifying, and thought to be helpful for easing catarrh and fighting infection. It goes well with vegetable juices in dips, soups and sauces.

Ginseng

The reason this is included is because it is popular as a tea and it goes very well with fruit juices as a warm or cold drink. In a concentrated form and under professional prescription, ginseng has many uses in oriental medicine. As a 'herbal' tea it is known as a general tonic and stimulant for helping to overcome fatigue. It helps when spirits are low and energy is lacking, when the pace of everyday life is too stressful and in times of great exertion. It is thought of as a balancing herb, both calming and stimulating according to the needs of the body.

Nuts and Seeds

These bring flavour and a change of texture to fruit and vegetable drinks, soups and sauces. They are superb with fruit and yogurt in smoothies or with lighter juice mixtures to enrich the fresh flavours slightly. They also contribute useful nutrients, such as vitamin E, thiamin, niacin, protein and calcium from sesame seeds for instance. Walnuts are even thought to help lower blood cholesterol levels in a diet with restricted intake of saturated fats.

Olive Oil

Extra-virgin olive oil can be used to enrich and flavour juices for savoury soups, dips, dressings and simple sauces. Olive oil is a monounsaturated fat and believed to make a positive contribution to the diet when used in modest amounts and to replace the majority of saturated fat.

Oats

Rolled oats make luscious smoothies when combined with fresh fruit – thoroughly puréed, they give drinks a creamy texture. As such they are good alternatives for those who cannot tolerate dairy produce. In the average balanced diet, they are simply a great storecupboard standby for making creamy drinks that are not high in fat. Oats are a good source of starchy carbohydrate and soluble fibre, believed to help with lowering cholesterol levels. They are also particularly practical for making mild-flavoured drinks as they can be used with unsweetened fruits that normally make milk curdle unless they are first combined with heavy syrups.

Rosewater

Rosewater is known as a popular home cosmetic for its astringent and refreshing qualities. It also goes very well with fruit and dairy products in a wide range of drinks. Its flavour and aroma have a calming and soothing effect, particularly for women as rosewater is associated with the pampering of beauty therapy.

Yogurt

Plain yogurt can be combined with fruit and vegetables without curdling to make smooth and tangy drinks. The slight tang of yogurt complements rich, sweet fruit, both fresh and dried. Live yogurt, or bio-yogurt, contains bacteria that are beneficial as they encourage a healthy environment in the gut and discourage the growth of bad or unwanted bacteria.

There is nothing complicated about preparing juice and you do not have to be a supercook to turn a few pieces of fruit or vegetable into a fabulous concoction. With anything practical, basic guidelines are helpful for getting the best out of techniques and avoiding pitfalls.

Juice or Purée?

There is a summary of juices and purées, and the ways in which they can be used, in the following section. To take a purist view, a juice is the liquid extracted from an ingredient, leaving behind the pulped flesh. A purée contains the juice and some or all of the flesh, depending on whether it has been pressed through a sieve.

To extract the juice from a purée, it has to be sieved or squeezed. Alternatively, a slightly thick purée can be thinned down to make a drink that contains both the juice and pulp. Whether you end up with a juice or a purée depends on the equipment and method you use. For the purpose of this book, both extracted juice and puréed ingredients in a thinned form are treated as 'juice'. The different textures and qualities are explained in the following section.

Equipment

A basic citrus squeezer may be enough to extract the juice from a couple of lemons or oranges, but you will need more than this to make the most of the juice available from the majority of fruit and vegetables.

Everyday Items

● A sharp cook's knife is essential for cutting and trimming fruit and vegetables.

● A grater with coarse or fine blades is used for removing citrus rind and it can also be used to grate fresh root ginger.

● A zester is quicker and easier than a grater for removing citrus rind in fine shreds. It is a small hand-held implement with a row of about 5 tiny, round cutting blades. Hold the fruit firmly in one hand and pull the zester across the skin to remove thin shreds of rind, leaving the pith behind. This is easier to wash than a grater.

● Citrus squeezers vary from a simple serrated club that extracts the juice when twisted into the flesh of the halved fruit to electric appliances. Typical hand-operated squeezers have a serrated dome on which to turn and press the fruit with a moat to collect the juice. The better types have a perforated moat and they rest over a container, allowing several fruit halves to be squeezed before the base has to be emptied; this type keeps all the pips and coarse bits of pulp separate. Electric squeezers rotate while the fruit halves are held on top, either by hand or by a cover. Electric squeezers have the advantage of being quick and easy, and extracting the most juice from the fruit.

● A sieve or strainer is useful for removing seeds or refining purées. This must be made from a non-reactive material, such as stainless steel or plastic.

● A balloon whisk or other simple hand whisk is useful for combining yogurt or other dairy products with juices.

● A flexible plastic spatula for scraping out every last drop of juice or smoothie from the mixing container.

Fine juice made in a juicer is essential for making cocktails and aperitifs using carrots, apples, pears, fennel, celery and similar coarse ingredients. To purée and then extract the juice from such fibrous ingredients is not only hard work, but the yield of juice compared to that from an electric juicer is small. An electric juicer is also excellent for preparing ginger juice.

Blender

Either a goblet blender or hand-held blender can be used for reducing fruit or vegetables and other ingredients to a pulp. With a little added liquid, the main ingredients are quickly reduced to a thin purée. This can be strained or sieved to give a fine juice or left as it is for a coarser juice.

A hand-held blender has the advantage of being easy to wash and a good choice for making individual drinks, but a tall and fairly slim jug is essential.

Electric Juicer

An electric juicer extracts the juice from the pulp and fibre. The fruit or vegetables are processed by a mixture of grating and spinning – rather like spin-drying. The juice is fine in texture but with a full, concentrated flavour. An electric juicer extracts the maximum amount of juice from ingredients. The flavour of the juice is intense and occasionally somewhat different from the basic ingredient – carrot juice is a good example. When carrots are put through an electric juicer they yield a deeply coloured, quite sweet juice with an intense flavour.

When using a juicer, always read and follow the manufacturer's directions. Cut the fruit into pieces of a suitable size for feeding into the machine and for it to process without straining the motor. When preparing a large quantity of juice, remove the pulp occasionally. Always empty the pulp at the end of juicing and thoroughly clean the machine.

Food Processors

Many food processors come with optional citrus squeezers. A food processor does not produce as fine a purée as a blender. This is particularly true when preparing slightly fibrous ingredients or tough vegetables, such as apples, pears, whole citrus fruit, fennel, celery or carrots. Soft foods, such as mango, peaches, tomatoes and dried fruits, can be reduced to fairly smooth juice in a food processor. The volume of liquid that can be processed in some machines is limited by the depth of the container around the central spindle (where the knife fits in place).

Selecting Ingredients

Only prime-quality produce should be used for juice: fresh, moist vegetables or fruit that is just ripe. Vegetables or fruit that are stale, limp or deteriorating are not suitable as they lack moisture and will yield only a small quantity of juice, usually of inferior flavour. Produce that is beginning to deteriorate and showing signs of decay or attack by mould should be discarded. Under-ripe fruit does not yield as much juice as ripe fruit and it does not have a good flavour.

Essentially, if the fruit looks good and tastes good as it is, it will juice well. If it looks dull and sad, has a poor aroma and flavour, then it will yield inferior juice. The choice of organic or non-organic ingredients is entirely personal. Using the freshest available is important. Making juice is a good way of using a generous harvest of home-grown produce

Many varieties of frozen fruit make good juices. Berries and currants, cooking apples, cherries and plums are good examples of fruit that can be frozen for juicing. Remember to remove the stones (pits) from cherries and plums before freezing. The fruit breaks down easily when puréed in a blender. Some frozen vegetables provide good juice – spinach and sugarsnap peas in particular.

Preparing Ingredients

The preparation method depends on the type of fruit or vegetable and the technique used to make the juice. When using a juice extractor, the preparation is also influenced by whether the leftover pulp is to be used or discarded.

If the fruit is puréed in a blender and all the pulp used, inedible skins, such as those on kiwi and mango, should be discarded. Similarly, if the pulp left in a juice extractor is to be used in a pickle, relish or sauce, then the vegetables or fruit should be trimmed before they are processed.

Peeling

Nutrients are concentrated in and under the skin or peel, so it is a good idea to scrub and trim fruit and vegetables with edible skins rather than peel them.

When using a juice extractor, there is no need to discard tender but inedible peel before processing. The juice extractor automatically separates the solid parts from the juice. There is no need to peel kiwi, mango or papaya, or other fruit with fairly tender but inedible skins.

Removing Cores, Seeds and Stones

When using a juice extractor and discarding the pulp, the cores can be left in apples and pears, but stones (pits) should be removed from cherries, plums and other stone fruit. Seeds should be removed from melons. Before puréeing in a blender, all inedible cores, seeds and stones should be removed.

Preventing Discoloration

Some fruits discolour when their flesh is exposed to the air – bananas, apples, pears and peaches are all examples. Tossing in lemon, lime or orange juice as the fruit is prepared prevents discoloration. Adding citrus juice when juicing or puréeing also helps to prevent the juice from deteriorating in colour if it is not used immediately.

Storing Fruit Juice

Since vitamins and other nutrients are lost when fruit is cut and/or allowed to become stale, the juice should be used as soon as it is prepared for maximum nutritional value. It is often more practical to prepare a batch of juice in the morning for use during the day or last thing at night ready for breakfast. Store the juice in an airtight container in the refrigerator.

Fruit juice freezes well. Chill the ingredients well before juicing them, then pour the juice straight into airtight containers and place in the freezer. It makes sense to freeze juice in small portions that thaw quickly – for example, in seconds or very few minutes in the microwave.

Preserving Nutrients

The nutritional value of fruit and vegetables is best in freshly harvested produce. Much of the goodness is found in and immediately under the skin or peel. The overall vitamin content diminishes with staleness; exposure to air, light and heat; and during cooking. For maximum value, fruit and vegetables should be as fresh as possible. Do not leave them to soak as water-soluble vitamins will be lost when the water is thrown away. Prepare fruit and vegetables when you are ready to use them, not in advance because cutting and exposing them to air diminishes the vitamin content. If you do cook any ingredients for juice, do this in the minimum liquid for the shortest time, and always use the cooking liquid as it contains dissolved nutrients.

*N*atural unsweetened fruit and vegetable juices should feature in the everyday diet. It is a good idea to have a repertoire of a few simple juices, served singly or in combination, that make affordable and easy daily drinks. Prepare the juice when you are ready to drink it or make a batch in the morning or last thing at night.

In addition to the standard juices for weekday breakfasts and to accompany meals, try experimenting with different juices when there is more time to spare at the weekend. Serve them as drinks, use them for soaking muesli or in savoury or sweet cooking.

Serve juice for a satisfying snack or as a tonic, for an additional nutrient boost in addition to your usual meals. Never rely on a juice drink as an alternative to a meal – juices may be full of goodness, but they do not provide a balanced mix of ingredients needed for a proper meal. Although hearty juice drinks are a terrific accompaniment for cereal, toast, muffins and/or fruit for breakfast, they are no more than a super-healthy snack.

Types of Juice

Juices can be used in many ways depending on their type.

Fine and Concentrated

Fine, full-flavoured juices prepared using a juice extractor are extremely versatile. They can be sipped as concentrated drinks or diluted with mineral water, buttermilk or yogurt. They may be served in savoury or sweet cocktails, used as mixers for alcoholic drinks, or combined with herb or spice tisanes.

Thin and Light

A juice extractor can be used to make thin juice that is light rather than concentrated by combining ingredients that have a high water content with others that give a concentrated flavour. For example, courgette, cucumber or marrow all yield a large quantity of lightly flavoured liquid that goes well with full-flavoured ingredients, extending and diluting them. Try them with carrots, apples, oranges, peaches or mangoes. Thin and light juices make refreshing long drinks. They can be topped up with a little sparkling mineral water to make refreshing drinks to go with meals. Light juices can also be prepared by puréeing and then sieving the ingredients.

Smooth and Luscious

Soft-textured fruit, smooth dairy produce, starchy oats and tender nuts, such as cashews and walnuts, make smooth and luscious drinks when puréed. These can be quite thick, depending on the level of fine juice, water or other liquid added. They are creamy and can be quite a treat.

Warming Juices

Fine juices can be mulled or combined with hot drinks, such as herb or spice infusions. Bananas are also excellent for making hot milky drinks – they sweeten the drink instead of adding sugar and contribute fruit goodness.

Thick and Wholesome

Almost any fruit or vegetable can be blended to a coarse purée, often with a little water added to make a drink. The consistency depends on the texture of the food and its water content. Crisp vegetables, such as fennel, carrot and pepper, produce coarse juices with a high fibre content and a texture similar to drinks containing finely crushed ice. The texture may seem a little strange at first but, once you are used to it, these drinks taste fabulous. They are packed with every last gram of goodness from the raw ingredients, including all-important fibre.

DRINKS FOR ALL OCCASIONS

DRINKS FOR ALL OCCASIONS

*I*t is easy to become quite hooked on juices. They are versatile and suitable for all occasions, and drinking them regularly imparts a fabulous sense of well-being. Simply preparing them gives a virtuous feeling of making the effort to be healthy!

Instead of feeling stuffed after a chocolate bar or gooey cream cake, you can get the same satisfaction from a luscious fruit smoothie combined with a sense of having given the body a vitamin boost. An exciting mix of fruit and vegetables whizzed into a pint-sized glass of goodness is refreshing and energizing after a work-out or other vigorous activity. When relaxation is the aim, a soothing fruit and herb drink is ideal for winding down the day. The following are some suggestions for types of juices for different occasions – but the choice is yours.

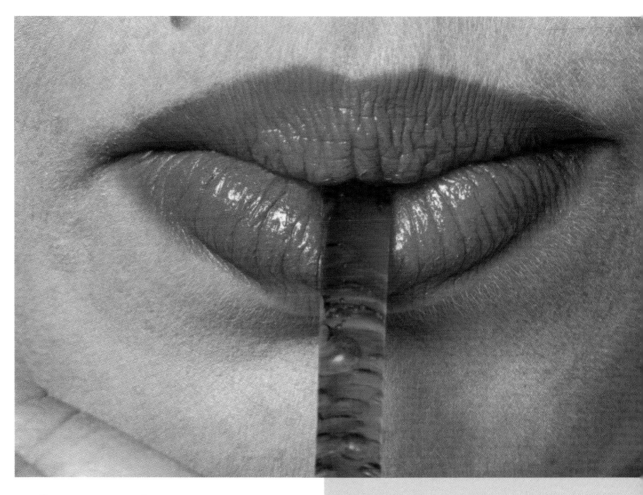

Breakfast Boosters

Try energizing citrus, berry, carrot and ginseng drinks for a fresh start. Add ginger or rosemary for lifting the spirits. Bananas, prunes, dried apricots, oats, yogurt and buttermilk bring real food value to morning drinks – make them thick and hearty if your only other breakfast food is a slice of toast. Whizz up a great big glass of bananas, berries, orange, oats and dried apricots spiked with some fresh root ginger and a sprinkling of mint, then top it off with a handful of toasted seeds and crunchy nuts to make breakfast on the move.

Between-meal Snacks

Apples, pears, mango, peaches, bananas and carrots all combine well in puréed juices that are hearty and satisfying. Thin them with mineral water or yogurt, or add citrus juice. For a savoury twist, try tomato, beetroot, fennel, celery or spinach in vegetable mixtures or with fruit – especially apples or pears. Flavour with uplifting herbs, such as basil, rosemary or mint, and add a sprinkling of sunny orange rind to give the spirits a boost.

DRINKS FOR ALL OCCASIONS

Light Meals

A fabulous mix of vegetables whizzed in a glass or a satisfying dairy smoothie makes a good alternative to a light lunch when time is short or it is simply too hot even to prepare and eat a sandwich. Do not skimp on the ingredients and use a variety so that you have as much in the juice as you would in a salad. Try apple, fennel, carrot, spring onions (scallions) and orange, rounded off with a handful of chopped watercress to make a drink that verges on a soup. Thin the mixture with water as you whizz it in a blender. Made with well-chilled ingredients and sipped through a thick straw, this type of drink is surprisingly filling and refreshing.

Meal-time Drinks

Prepare light fruit or vegetable juices, singly or in simple combinations, and dilute them with water to make refreshing accompaniments for main meals. Citrus, apple, pear, melon, grape, fennel or celery all have delicate flavours that will not clash with cooked dishes.

DRINKS FOR ALL OCCASIONS

Alternative Aperitifs

Try full-flavoured juices from an extractor for grown-up vitamin cocktails to sip before dinner. Tomato is the classic – try it with lime and mint or a hint of coriander (cilantro) instead of (or as well as) vodka. Carrot and red or orange pepper can be sharpened with lemon juice and pepped up with the tiniest pinch of cayenne pepper. Cherry and pineapple are vibrant neat or topped up to make a long cooler. Exotic passion fruit is perfect when served short, with a little papaya and orange. Introduce a lively flavour by adding fresh root ginger to popular mango.

System Clearing

Any and every fruit and vegetable drink helps when you feel the need for detoxifying your system. Celery, fennel and lemon make a terrific combination – whizz them with mineral water or with extra orange juice for a thirst-quenching drink. Juniper is a wintry spice that has a reputation for helping to cleanse the system – mull orange and apple with juniper and cinnamon to promote cleansing and good circulation. Herb infusions invariably aid digestion – try parsley with pineapple, tarragon with carrot juice, or angelica with lemon and white grape juice.

Invigorating Extras

Make the most of fresh-flavoured herbs and spices with light juices for refreshing drinks. For example, combine refreshing mint, cucumber and head-clearing cardamom with lively lemon and lime in a drink to awake the senses. Beetroot juice is a traditional tonic and it tastes fabulous with raspberry or blackcurrant. Down a green vegetable drink for a drink full of plant goodness – try broccoli, spinach and spring onions (scallions), adding a fine-skinned lime for fruity zestiness.

Relaxing and Calming

When you plan time out to pamper yourself, remember to include a suitable drink. Try a smoothie with papaya, raspberries, yogurt and rosewater, or guava and pear with a little buttermilk. To help overcome stress or calm down when life is hectic, combine calming celery with apple and lemon, or grape juice with camomile tea.

OTHER JUICE IDEAS

OTHER JUICE IDEAS

ruit and vegetable juices are so
tempting that they rarely make it
beyond a glass, but there are lots
of other ways of using them to bring
vitamins, minerals and phytochemicals into
your daily diet.

Soups

Vegetable juices make quick and easy soups. Simply stir-fry some chopped spring onions (scallions), crushed garlic cloves and some grated lemon rind in a little olive oil for about 3 minutes, then add the vegetable juice and heat gently until simmering. Season and add a handful of chopped fresh herbs – such as parsley, basil and tarragon. Try this method with carrot, tomato, fennel, cucumber, celery, beetroot or broccoli juices, singly or in any combination. Swirl a little plain yogurt through the soup in the bowl for a creamy finish.

As well as savoury soups, fruit soups make stylish alternatives to rich desserts. They seem sophisticated and dinner guests will be impressed, but they are simply smoothies. Make your favourite fruit smoothie and serve it in glass dishes or fine china bowls, then top it with a few pieces of fresh fruit and some shredded mint for a decorative flourish. Try mango and lychee; peach and passion fruit; pear, lime and ginger; or cherry and apple.

OTHER JUICE IDEAS

Sauces

Instead of adding stock or water to casseroles, try carrot, tomato, celery or fennel juice, or a mixture of vegetable juices. Remember to season the casserole well or replace only part of the stock instead of the entire quantity. Vegetable juices go well in most poultry casseroles and with pork, lamb or venison. Apple or orange juice are also excellent with rich meat, such as pork or lamb.

Use apple, orange or carrot juice to deglaze the pan after cooking meat – simply add the juice and cook, stirring, over a high heat until the liquor boils and reduces in a flavoursome sauce.

Many fruit juices go well with olive oil in simple salad dressings – try orange and lime as well as the popular lemon.

Sweet Dishes and Desserts

Use fresh fruit juices to make syrups by dissolving sugar in a little of the juice in a saucepan, then allowing it to cool before adding the remaining juice. Serve syrups instead of rich creams and custards. Whizz dried fruit, such as apricots or peaches, with fresh fruit (strawberries, raspberries or kiwi fruit, for example) to make thick juices that can be served as instant sauces with ice cream, sponge puddings or pancakes.

Use fruit juices to make sweet sauces by cooking them with a little arrowroot or cornflour (cornstarch) and adding a little honey or sugar. Purée apple or orange juice with plain unsalted cashew nuts or almonds, adding the juice a little at a time to the finely ground nuts, to make a luscious alternative to dairy cream.

Fruit juices can be used to make super jellies and creams. Soak rolled oats with lively fruit juice and enrich with yogurt. Soak home-made muesli in apple, orange, melon or pineapple juice overnight for a fruity breakfast.

OTHER JUICE IDEAS

Bought Juice

Bought juice can be used to supplement or extend home-made juices, for example, bought apple or orange juice is useful for extending home-juiced exotic fruit or vegetables. The advantage of making juice just when you are ready to drink it is not just that it tastes better but it also retains as much nutritional value as possible. In the real world, when time is often short, bought juice is better than no juice at all; both commercial and home-made juices are complementary in a balanced diet.

It is important to distinguish between the juices and drinks that are available. Freshly squeezed juices are sold in the chiller cabinet and they have a short shelf life. Long-life juices are made from concentrated extracts and they are heat-treated for preservation. Whether you are buying chilled or long-life products, be sure to check their content because 'juice drinks' usually have sugar (sometimes lots of it) and are mixed with rather expensive water. They may also contain flavourings and colouring ingredients. So read the labels carefully to ensure you are paying for juice and not diluted juice with flavoured water; some fruit juice drinks contain only a small percentage of juice.

OTHER JUICE IDEAS

Simply Savoury

Vibrant Carotene Cocktail

Pick up a Pepper

Pina Beetroot

Cucumber Cooler

B and O

Red Sensation

Speedy Gazpacho

Simple Green Soup

**Avocado, Watercress
and Apple Soup**

Tomato and Orange Soup

OTHER JUICE IDEAS

Vibrant Carotene Cocktail

The colour says it all for this cocktail – it is packed with the protective power of beta carotene and vitamin C from the carrots and orange peppers. A little fresh root ginger cuts the sweetness of the vegetables.

Serves 1

300 g/10 oz/carrots
1 large orange (bell) pepper
1 thin slice fresh root ginger

Chill all the ingredients in advance. Extract the juice from the carrots, orange pepper and ginger. Stir well and serve at once.

OTHER JUICE IDEAS

Pick up a Pepper

This is simplicity itself and a glassful of vitamin C goodness. It is the perfect recipe for a hand-held blender – do not be tempted to strain out the fine bits of pepper as they are full of fibre goodness.

Serves 1

I small to medium green (bell) pepper,
seeded and cut into chunks
125 ml/4 fl oz/½ cup sweet apple juice

Blend the green pepper and apple juice to a smooth, frothy drink. If using a hand-held blender, pump it up and down in the goblet to create a creamy froth. Serve at once.

OTHER JUICE IDEAS

Pina Beetroot

Beetroot juice has an old-fashioned reputation for being a tonic and pineapple was thought to be a cure-all fruit. This may seem rather fanciful, but this drink provides a glassful of plant-food goodness that tastes fabulous. This is a good example of how bought fruit juice can be used to complement home-made juice – the pineapple juice can be squeezed from fresh fruit or bought ready made.

Serves 1

150 g/5 oz/raw beetroot, trimmed and thinly peeled
1 yellow (bell) pepper, quartered lengthways
125 ml/4 fl oz/½ cup pineapple juice

Juice the beetroot and yellow pepper, then stir in the pineapple juice and serve.

Variation Cooked beetroot can be used instead of the raw vegetable. Red (bell) pepper can be used instead of yellow for a stronger flavour.

OTHER JUICE IDEAS

Cucumber Cooler

Make this cleansing and refreshing drink on hot summer days or as an antidote to stuffy central-heated winter environments. Mint, cardamom and lemon bring lively complementary flavours and stomach-calming characteristics to cooling cucumber.

Serves 1

2 green cardamoms
1 lemon
2 large fresh mint sprigs
7.5 cm (3 inch) piece cucumber, cut into chunks
200 ml/7 fl oz/¾ cup water
1 teaspoon honey (optional)

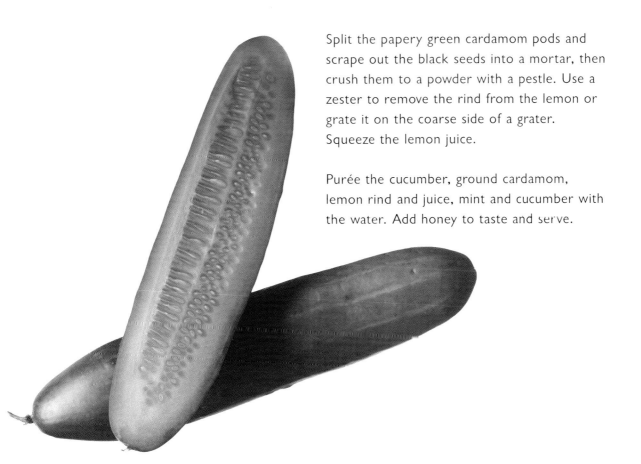

Split the papery green cardamom pods and scrape out the black seeds into a mortar, then crush them to a powder with a pestle. Use a zester to remove the rind from the lemon or grate it on the coarse side of a grater. Squeeze the lemon juice.

Purée the cucumber, ground cardamom, lemon rind and juice, mint and cucumber with the water. Add honey to taste and serve.

OTHER JUICE IDEAS

B and O

Broccoli and orange, heavily laced with dill or fennel, makes an antioxidant-rich drink with all the goodness of the cruciferous vegetables thought to be helpful in preventing cancer. Drink this before a meal, instead of a first course, or as a quick snack while you are cooking after-work dinner.

Serves 1

125 g/4 oz/broccoli
2 oranges
200 ml/7 fl oz/¾ cup water
handful of fresh dill or fennel sprigs, chopped

Break the broccoli into florets. Use a zester to remove the rind from 1 orange or grate it on the coarse side of a grater. Squeeze the juice from both oranges, then blend it with the broccoli and orange rind until smooth. Gradually add the water with the motor running. Add the dill or fennel and blend briefly before serving.

OTHER JUICE IDEAS

Red Sensation

This is a real winner and guaranteed to convert newcomers to vegetable juices. Served as a savoury smoothie in a tall glass, it is slightly creamy and sophisticated, and full of antioxidant goodness from the beta carotene in the carrots. Lycopene, the carotenoid found in tomatoes, is thought to help prevent prostate cancer. Horseradish is a traditional aid to digestion and a diuretic; it is also thought to have antibiotic properties and is helpful in curing urinary infections.

Serves 1

125 ml/4 fl oz/½ cup carrot juice
125 ml/4 fl oz/½ tomato juice
½ teaspoon hot horseradish sauce
2 tablespoons plain yogurt

Place all the ingredients in a jug and whisk until thoroughly mixed. Pour into a tall glass and serve.

Straight and Spicy Omit the yogurt and increase the quantity of horseradish sauce to 1 teaspoon. Serve in 2 cocktail glasses.

Rich Red Soup The drink can be served as a refreshing chilled soup – it will provide one generous portion. Double the quantity for two or make four times the amount to serve six as a dinner party starter. Swirl a little extra yogurt in the soup as a garnish and sprinkle with finely snipped chives.

OTHER JUICE IDEAS

Speedy Gazpacho

Gazpacho is a cold Spanish soup of fresh vegetables and tomatoes, seasoned with garlic, enriched with olive oil and thickened with bread. It tastes fabulous and it makes a hearty, healthy lunch. It is just packed with vegetable goodness: antioxidant vitamins C and E, and beta carotene; protective lycopene from the tomatoes; allicin from the garlic and onion; and in this recipe some wholemeal bread for satisfying fibre-rich carbohydrate. Make the tomato juice when you have a glut or buy it ready made. Have all the ingredients well chilled and the soup will be ready to serve in just a few minutes.

Blend the onion, garlic, cucumber, green and red pepper to a purée. Add the bread, about a third of the tomato juice and the olive oil, then blend until smooth. Add the remaining tomato juice and blend briefly or transfer the purée to a bowl and stir in the remaining tomato juice. Stir in seasoning to taste and serve chilled. Sprinkle a little diced pepper, cucumber, sliced olives and croûtons over each portion, offering extra toppings in small dishes so that they can be added as the soup is eaten.

Serves 4

1 onion, roughly chopped
2 garlic cloves, peeled
5 cm/2 inch/piece cucumber, cut into chunks
1 green (bell) pepper, seeded and cut into chunks
1 red (bell) pepper, seeded and cut into chunks
1 thick slice wholemeal bread, diced
900 ml/1½ pints/3¾ cups tomato juice
3 tablespoons olive oil
salt and freshly ground black pepper

To serve

1 green (bell) pepper, seeded and diced
5 cm/2 inch/piece cucumber, diced
black olives, sliced
bread croûtons

Simple Green Soup

This is full of fresh green flavours and packed with vegetable goodness, especially folate and the cancer-fighting benefits of broccoli. Frozen peas are so common that they are dismissed for all but the dullest of meals – which is a great shame, because they are full of flavour and nutrients. They have far more vitamin C than raw peas on sale in the supermarket.

Serves 4

200 ml/7 fl oz/¾ cup water
225 g/8 oz/1¾ cups frozen peas
1 slice white bread, cut into chunks
2 green (bell) peppers, seeded and cut into chunks
225 g/8 oz/broccoli, roughly chopped
2 garlic cloves, peeled
1 pickling onion, peeled
2 tablespoons olive oil
handful of soft basil sprigs
salt and freshly ground black pepper

Bring the water to the boil in a small saucepan. Add the peas, then remove from the heat and leave to stand for a couple of minutes. Strain the peas and pour the water over the bread in a bowl. Purée the peas with the green peppers, broccoli, garlic and pickling onion. Then add the bread and water, olive oil and basil and continue to blend until smooth. Add seasoning to taste and chill before serving.

Avocado, Watercress and Apple Soup

Fresh, fruity apple juice is excellent in cold soups instead of stock. It goes particularly well with avocado and lemon in this lightly spiced soup. Avocado is a good source of vitamin E, a valuable antioxidant vitamin, and the watercress contributes folate and iron to the soup. Vitamin C from the apple and lemon juice helps the body to absorb the iron from the watercress.

Serves 4

1 lemon
2 avocados
1 bunch of watercress
1 garlic clove, peeled (optional)
2 spring onions (scallions), chopped
475 ml/16 fl oz/2 cups freshly squeezed apple juice

Squeeze the juice from the lemon and place in a blender. Halve the avocados, remove their stones (pits) and add the flesh to the blender with the watercress, garlic (if using), spring onions and about a third of the apple juice. Blend until smooth, then gradually add the remaining apple juice with the motor running. Serve at once.

Variation For a creamy soup, add 200 ml/7 fl oz/¾ cup Greek-style yogurt and blend briefly.

OTHER JUICE IDEAS

Tomato and Orange Soup

This is simple and delicious either hot or cold. Serve it as a vitamin-rich snack or in mugs as an accompaniment for sandwiches to make a well-balanced lunch.

Serves 4

1 tablespoon olive oil
1 bunch of spring onions (scallions), chopped
2 tablespoons fresh thyme leaves
900 ml/1½ pints/3¾ cups tomato juice
2 oranges
salt and freshly ground black pepper

Place the olive oil, spring onions and thyme in a large saucepan. Cook over medium heat for about 5 minutes, until the onions are softened. Stir in the tomato juice and heat gently. Meanwhile use a zester or coarse grater to remove the rind from 1 orange, then squeeze the juice from both fruit. When the soup comes to the boil, remove it from the heat and add the orange rind and juice. Stir in seasoning to taste and serve at once.

Chilled Tomato and Orange Soup

Chill the tomato juice and the oranges before juicing them. Cook the spring onions and thyme as above, then remove them from the heat and leave to cool slightly. Stir in the chilled tomato juice with the orange rind and juice.

Carrot and Orange Soup This is also delicious made with carrot juice instead of tomato juice. For a creamy carrot soup, heat the soup gently for a few seconds after adding the orange juice. Then remove from the heat and stir in 150 ml/¼ pint/⅔ cup plain yogurt with some freshly chopped tarragon.

OTHER JUICE IDEAS

Drink to Good Health

Spicy Fruit Whizz

Breakfast Fix

Apricot and Orange Froth

Fennel and Grape Reviver

Sage-scented Apricot Cooler

Rosemary Apple Energizer

Glorious and Green

Mango and Carrot Silk

Curious Kiwi

Mellow Yellow

Red Quencher

Celery, Apple and Cucumber Cooler

Spicy Prune Citrus

Tomato Start

OTHER JUICE IDEAS

Spicy Fruit Whizz

Blackcurrants are an old-fashioned 'full-of-goodness food', long appreciated as a rich source of vitamin C. Their protective and anti-inflammatory properties have earned them a reputation for guarding against winter colds and, along with honey and lemon, helping to soothe sore throats. Combined with apple for sweetness and ginger for a warming yet refreshing result, they taste fabulous in a drink that helps to ward off chills and colds or at least ease the symptoms when it is too late to avoid the infection.

Serves 1

60 g/2 oz/½ cup blackcurrants
1 tablespoon grated fresh root ginger
1 sweet dessert apple, cored and cut into chunks
200 ml/7 fl oz/¾ cup water

Use a fork to scrape the blackcurrants off their stalks. Blend them with the ginger, apple and water until smooth.

Lightly Gingered The ginger used above gives the drink a real kick – fantastic when the drink is served really cold – but for a less hot flavour use 1–2 teaspoons grated fresh root ginger instead.

Warming Honey Comforter For a warming drink, purée the fruit with 1 teaspoon honey but without the water. Then stir in 200 ml/7 fl oz/¾ cup boiling water.

Zingy Smoothie For a super-lively smoothie, stir 4 tablespoons low-fat fromage frais into the blended mixture and serve as a morning-call cocktail – it is a fabulous way to start the day!

OTHER JUICE IDEAS

Breakfast Fix

If you have never been a great fan of carrot juice, this drink will change your opinion and have you craving more. It makes a wonderful summery wake-up concoction, with a wonderfully zesty flavour and, when the ingredients go straight from refrigerator to blender, a texture resembling crushed ice. For a healthy breakfast, serve this vitamin-rich drink with wholemeal toast, a bowl of muesli or another cereal for daily fibre and a banana for energy and potassium.

Serves 1

1 lime
1 carrot, diced
1 sweet dessert apple, cored and cut into chunks
150 ml/¼ pint/⅔ cup water

Use a zester to pare the rind off the lime or grate it coarsely. Cut off and discard the rest of the peel under the bright green rind, then halve the lime and cut it into chunks, discarding any pips. Blend the lime and its rind with the carrot, apple and water until the mixture resembles a fine sludge. Serve in a tall glass or a deep bowl, with a spoon or a wide drinking straw.

Fine Fix Use a juicer to make a fine, smooth drink. Alternatively, press the mixture through a fine sieve.

Breakfast Grapefruit Use 1 grapefruit instead of the lime, selecting a pink fruit for a sweeter result.

OTHER JUICE IDEAS

Apricot and Orange Froth

This tangy, light and refreshing drink is good at any time of the day and the ideal alternative to an alcoholic aperitif. It provides vitamin C and beta carotene, along with some fibre from the orange.

Serves 1

1 large orange, peeled and roughly chopped
3 apricots, halved and stoned (pitted)
sparkling mineral water

Discard any pips from the orange, then purée it with the apricots until smooth. Pour into a tall glass and top up with sparkling mineral water.

Orange and Nectarine Froth
Use 1 ripe nectarine instead of the apricots.

Orange and Peach Froth
Use 1 ripe peach instead of the apricots.

Orange and Apricot Smoothie
Briefly blend 200 ml/7 fl oz/¾ cup thin low-fat yogurt with the fruit purée. Pour into a tall glass and sprinkle with a mixture of brown sugar and a pinch of ground cinnamon.

OTHER JUICE IDEAS

Fennel and Grape Reviver

Slightly aniseed fennel marries with bitter lemon and sweet grapes in a drink designed to make you feel a million dollars – it tastes gorgeous. Drinking it imparts a sense of well-being – rather like eating a really tasty salad – and brings a boost of valuable nutrients to the diet, with vitamin C from the lemon and potassium from the grapes. Fennel provides beta carotene, folate and plant hormones thought to help ease menopausal problems; it also acts as a diuretic and helps to balance premenstrual water retention.

Serves 1

½ head of fennel, roughly chopped
150 g/5 oz/1 cup sweet seedless green grapes
2 thin lemon slices
150 ml/5 fl oz/⅔ cup water

Purée the fennel with grapes, lemon slices (discard any pips, but include the peel) and water until smooth.

Mint Reviver Add the leaves from 2 mint sprigs.

Lime Reviver Use 2 thin lime slices instead of the lemon.

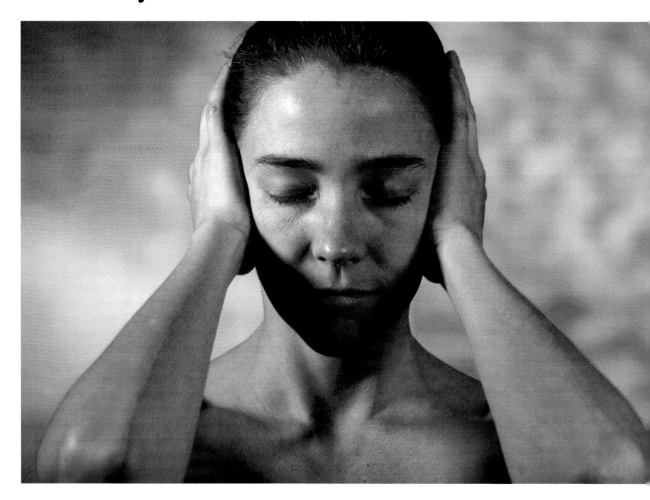

Sage-scented Apricot Cooler

Like many herbs, sage has an ancient reputation for its beneficial properties. It is used in tisanes and mouthwashes to ease infections of the throat and mouth, and it is generally thought of as a herb to aid digestion and healing. It is also considered to be beneficial in relieving headaches, and overcoming stress and anxiety. In a simple sense there is something reassuring about the warm, slightly peppery tone that sage brings to this otherwise plain mixture of fruit juice.

Serves 2

1 orange, peeled and roughly chopped
4 apricots, halved and stoned (pitted)
5 large fresh sage leaves
125 ml/4 fl oz/½ cup water
sparkling mineral water

Discard the pips from the orange, then purée it with the apricots, sage and water. Divide between 2 glasses and top up with a little sparkling mineral water.

Sweet Sage Cooler For a sweeter drink and to accentuate the sage flavour, place the orange and apricots in a small bowl. Shred the sage leaves and sprinkle them over the fruit, then sprinkle with 2 teaspoons soft brown sugar. Cover and chill for at least 30 minutes or for several hours, to allow the juices from the fruit to run and mingle with the sage. Purée and finish as above.

Sage-scented Fruit Juice Use a mixture of 125 ml/4 fl oz/½ cup each of orange juice and apricot juice. Finely shred the sage with scissors, adding it straight to the juice, then top up with sparkling mineral water.

OTHER JUICE IDEAS

Rosemary Apple Energizer

The flavour of the rosemary is quite elusive in this sharp fruit drink that makes an energy-boosting reviver to lift the spirits during the low periods in a day. Rosemary has an age-old reputation for stimulating the nervous system and boosting brain function, at the same time improving memory. It is also known as a natural antiseptic, good for mouthwashes and gargles to help soothe a sore throat. Its aromatic properties are also appreciated and it has a reputation for clearing a stuffy head – especially when added to a bowl of very hot water and used as an inhalant.

Serves 1

1 large soft rosemary sprig
1 apple, cored and roughly chopped
¼ – ½ lime, roughly chopped
1 teaspoon honey
200 ml/7 fl oz/¾ cup water

Pick the soft spiky leaves off the rosemary sprig and chop them, then purée them with the apple, lime (including all the peel), honey and water.

When adding the lime, half the fruit brings a pleasing bitter flavour to the drink, but for a tangy, rather than bitter, flavour reduce this to a quarter. Alternatively, grate the rind off the fruit, then peel off and discard the white pith before roughly chopping the flesh; add the flesh and rind to the apple.

OTHER JUICE IDEAS

Summer Soup

This simple drink is easily transformed into an impressive cold first course. Purée 1 large green pepper, 3 kiwi fruit and 10 ready-to-eat dried apricots, with 2 avocados, the juice of 1 lemon, 150 ml/¼ pint/⅔ cup water and 150 ml/¼ pint/⅔ cup plain yogurt. The soup should be quite thick, but it can be thinned with a little extra water, if necessary. Serve sprinkled with a little chopped dill or tarragon.

Glorious and Green

A little green pepper brings a savoury twist to sweet dried apricots and fruity kiwi in this super drink. It is as good for you as it tastes and absolutely packed with nutrients. Dried apricots are a great source of goodness, providing iron, potassium and beta carotene. Between them, kiwi and green pepper offer a super-boost of vitamin C as well as folate, carotene and fibre.

Serves 1

½ small green (bell) pepper, seeded and cut into chunks
1 kiwi fruit, peeled and cut into chunks
6 ready-to-eat dried apricots, quartered
150 ml/¼ pint/⅔ cup water

Purée all the ingredients until smooth, then pour into a large glass.

Mango and Carrot Silk

When making juice, carrots and inexpensive apples are good for bulking out the more expensive fruit. They also contribute valuable vitamins and carrot juice is packed with beta carotene. Sip this juice neat, as a concentrated cocktail, or top it up with a little sparkling mineral water for a lighter, longer cooler.

I small mango
3 large carrots

Peel the mango if you intend using the pulp for making a salsa or relish; if not, then leave the peel on. Cut the flesh off the stone (pit), then cut it into chunks. Trim the carrots and peel them if using the pulp. Extract the juice from the fruit and pour it into a small glass. Alternatively, pour the juice into a medium-sized glass and top it up with sparkling mineral water.

Mango and Carrot Buttermilk
Top up the juice with an equal quantity of buttermilk.

Golden Yogurt Drink Gradually whisk
the mango and carrot juice into 150 ml/¼ pint/⅔ cup plain yogurt to make a smooth and fruity dairy drink.

OTHER JUICE IDEAS

Curious Kiwi

Fresh or frozen chopped spinach can be used for this remarkably good drink with a flavour that is best described as just moving away from fruity towards savoury. Although spinach is rich in iron, it is not in a form that the body can access easily; however, vitamin C from the kiwi fruit helps the body to absorb as much as possible. Spinach makes a valuable folate contribution.

> 2 kiwi fruit, peeled and cut into chunks
> 2 slices of lime, with peel
> 125 g/4 oz/¾ cup spinach, chopped

Purée the ingredients until smooth, then strain the juice through a fine sieve. Press and turn the pulp to extract all the juice without actually pressing or rubbing it through the sieve. Pour into a glass and serve at once.

Delicious Green Dip or Sauce
Do not discard the pulp but use it to make a delicious dip or a sauce to serve on pasta. Turn the pulp into a bowl and stir in 1 crushed garlic clove, 4 finely chopped spring onions (scallions), 4 tablespoons freshly grated Parmesan cheese and 2 tablespoons extra-virgin olive oil. Add 150 ml/¼ pint/⅔ cup fromage frais and shred a handful of basil leaves into the bowl, then season to taste and stir well.

Curiously Fruity For a drink that is far more fruity than savoury, add an additional kiwi fruit.

Mellow Yellow

This light and bright juice is packed with vitamin C that plays a vital protective role and helps the body to absorb and use other nutrients. It makes a good sipping drink as an aperitif – terrific with crudités and dips or healthy snacks – or it can be further diluted and served as a long drink with lunch.

Serves 1

1 yellow (bell) pepper, seeded and cut in chunks
1 nectarine, halved, stoned (pitted) and quartered
125 ml/4 fl oz/½ cup water

Extract the juice from the pepper and nectarine. Pour the water through the juicer or add it to the juice at the end, depending on the manufacturer's directions.

Peachy Purée Use a ripe peach instead of the nectarine and purée the ingredients instead of extracting their juice.

Mango and Pepper Juice Use a small mango instead of the nectarine.

Yellow Plum and Pepper Juice
Use 4 yellow plums instead of the nectarine.

OTHER JUICE IDEAS

Scrape the currants off their stalks using a fork. Then purée them with the beetroot and carrot until smooth. Add the water and blend briefly.

Rich Red Juice Alternatively, extract the juice from the ingredients to make a smooth, fine and rich drink.

Red Quencher

Sweet beetroot and carrots perfectly complement the tart redcurrants that bring a fruity flavour to this thirst-quenching drink. The flavour is fabulous, the colour vibrant and the feel-good sensation the drink induces is supported by its nutritional value. Beetroot is rich in potassium and folate, and it also provides vitamin C. The redcurrants contribute vitamin C, iron and potassium; and the carrots bring beta carotene to the drink. The result is a real tonic.

Serves 1

60 g/2 oz/½ cup redcurrants
75 g (2½ oz) ⅓ cup cooked beetroot, cut into chunks
1 large carrot, diced
3 – 4 tablespoons water

OTHER JUICE IDEAS

Serves 1

1 celery stick, cut into chunks
1 large sweet, full-flavoured dessert apple, cored and cut
    into chunks
5 cm/2 inch/piece cucumber, quartered lengthways
lemonade

Extract the juice from the celery, apple and cucumber. Pour into a glass and top up with lemonade.

Celery, Apple and Cucumber Cooler

Fresh fruit and vegetable juices make super cooling drinks when diluted with lemonade. Topping up neat juice with lemonade is a good way of acquainting your palate with vegetable flavours that can taste slightly unusual at first. Use a low-sugar lemonade or tonic water so as not to drown the natural flavours. Celery is a good source of potassium and a diuretic; it is also used in traditional medicine to promote efficient kidney function and to help relieve the painful symptoms of gout. However, celery does accumulate nitrate found naturally in the soil or from fertilizers, so it is not a good idea to consume large quantities of the vegetable regularly.

OTHER JUICE IDEAS

Spicy Prune Citrus

Dried fruit is a valuable source of goodness in fruit drinks. Prunes make a rich and satisfying drink that brings potassium and iron to the diet as well as fibre for avoiding or overcoming constipation. They are also a good source of natural fruit sugar for energy.

Serves 2

1 small thin-skinned lemon
8 ready-to-eat dried prunes
2 slices fresh root ginger, peeled
350 ml/12 fl oz/1½ cups water

Roughly chop the lemon, picking out and discarding the pips as you do so. Purée the lemon with the prunes, ginger and 150 ml/¼ pint/⅔ cup of the water until smooth. Gradually add the remaining water with the blender running.

Variation The whole lemon brings a strong citrus tang to the drink; for a less-sharp result, pare or grate the rind off the fruit, then squeeze the juice and purée these with the prunes.

OTHER JUICE IDEAS

Tomato Start

Tomato juice is an old-fashioned ingredient for hangover drinks, usually in ghastly concoctions that seem more like punishment than comfort cures for a bad head. This is quite the opposite – nothing at all to do with curing alcohol poisoning, but a great alternative to the spirits that cause it. Lively grapefruit and tomatoes bring vitamins C and E to the breakfast menu. The carotene substance in tomatoes – lycopene – is thought to be beneficial in preventing prostrate cancer.

Serves 1

125 ml/4 fl oz/½ cup tomato juice
200 ml/7 fl oz/¾ cup grapefruit juice
pinch of cayenne pepper (optional)

Mix the tomato and grapefruit juices. Season with a hint of cayenne pepper, if liked.

Variation Alter the emphasis from morning to evening by using 200 ml/7 fl oz/3/4 cup tomato juice and 100 ml/4 fl oz/1/2 cup grapefruit juice for an early evening cocktail. Enliven the juice by topping with ? teaspoon finely chopped fresh root ginger mixed with fine shreds of grapefruit rind, removed with a zester, and a little freshly chopped coriander (cilantro).

OTHER JUICE IDEAS

Perfect Smoothies

Blackcurrant and Orange Oaty

Apricot Pecan Smoothie

Banana and Orange Breakfast

Snack in a Glass

Fruit and Vegetable Smoothie

Banana and Ginger Milk

Mango and Strawberry Swirl

Strawberry Oat Crush

Nutty Nectarine Whip

Blackcurrant and Orange Oaty

Thick and creamy, this is a terrific alternative to dairy-based smoothies. It makes a brilliant breakfast drink or snack at any time of day, providing plenty of vitamin C and a useful shot of soluble fibre from the rolled oats. Leave it slightly lumpy to retain all the fibre the fruit also has to offer and it is especially satisfying.

Serves 1

60 g/2 oz/½ cup blackcurrants
1 orange, peeled and roughly chopped
3 tablespoons rolled oats
125 ml/4 fl oz/½ cup water

Use a fork to scrape the blackcurrants off their stalks. Blend them to a smooth purée with the orange – picking out and discarding any pips – oats and a little of the water. Add the remaining water, whizz again and pour into a large glass. Thin with a little extra water if required.

Blackcurrant and Apple Oaty
For a thinner drink, omit the orange and use 200 ml/7 fl oz/¾ cup apple juice instead of the water.

Redcurrant and Satsuma Oaty
Use redcurrants instead of blackcurrants and the segments from 2 satsumas instead of the orange.

OTHER JUICE IDEAS

Apricot Pecan Smoothie

Take time out from a busy day to relax over this soothing smoothie which is luscious, tangy and deliciously nutty. It is also just the drink for helping to combat stress and counteract the wear and tear of modern living. As well as vitamin C and fibre, apricots offer beta carotene, the protective antioxidant which the body can also convert into vitamin A. Nuts provide B vitamins, part of whose function is to ensure the body can release the energy from food and maintain a healthy nervous system.

Serves 1

3 ripe apricots, halved and stoned (pitted)
30 g/1 oz/¼ cup shelled pecan nuts
150 ml/¼ pint/⅔ cup mild plain yogurt, such as Greek style yogurt
125 ml/4 fl oz/½ cup water

Purée the apricots, pecan nuts and yogurt until smooth. Add the water and whizz briefly before serving.

Slightly Sweet Smoothie The flavour of the smoothie depends on the sweetness of the apricots and the type of yogurt used. Use tangy yogurt and sharp fruit to make a drink with a sharp edge – stir in a trickle of maple syrup (to taste) to complement the nutty flavour of the smoothie and sweeten it slightly.

Simple Dessert Topping Omit the water and sweeten the purée with a little maple syrup or honey, then serve as a tempting dessert sauce with grilled fruit kebabs, cheesecake, sponge puddings or a wide variety of desserts.

OTHER JUICE IDEAS

Serves 1

1 large juicy orange, peeled and cut into chunks
1 banana, cut into chunks
150 ml/¼ pint/⅔ cup plain yogurt

Discard any pips from the orange, then just whizz it with the banana and yogurt until smooth.

Breakfast Mash Squeeze the juice from 2 oranges or use 200 ml/7 fl oz/¾ cup orange juice instead of the whole orange. Mash the banana with the yogurt, then stir in the juice.

Banana and Orange Breakfast

Although this luscious concoction tastes wonderfully indulgent, it does the body a favour first thing in the morning, providing fibre, energy and potassium in the banana, vitamin C in the orange, and dairy goodness, including calcium, in the yogurt. The bacteria found in live, bio-yogurt are also thought to be beneficial in promoting good bacterial balance in the gut, helping it to function well. When faddy teenagers or children do not want to spare time for breakfast, offering them a fashionable drink can be a tempting alternative – and this is a good recipe for sneaking in lots of sensible nutrients.

OTHER JUICE IDEAS

Snack in a Glass

Black grapes bring antioxidants and potassium to this simple creamy drink which is enriched with carrot for depth of flavour and colour, as well as beta carotene goodness. It makes a good morning drink, for example to complement a bowl of cereal or toast and piece of fruit for breakfast, or a satisfying and healthy between-meal snack.

Serves 1

1 large carrot, cut into chunks
150 g/5 oz/1 cup sweet seedless black or red grapes
125 ml/4 fl oz/½ cup water
4 tablespoons plain yogurt

Purée the carrot, grapes and water until smooth, then add the yogurt and blend for a few seconds.

Spicy Snack in a Glass Sprinkle the drink with a little freshly grated nutmeg before serving for a spicy flavour.

Apple and Grape Snack Use a large dessert apple instead of the carrot, removing the core but retaining the peel.

OTHER JUICE IDEAS

Fruit and Vegetable Smoothie

Vegetables are often overlooked as ingredients for smoothies, but they make lightly flavoured interesting drinks, especially when combined with fruit. Many are rather like summer soups and would not be out of place as a first course – this mix is a good example as it goes well with a sandwich for a light lunch or late supper. It is also a healthy alternative to a bag of crisps or a chocolate bar for a quick after-work snack while making dinner or before dashing out.

Serves 2

3 kiwi fruit, peeled and cut into chunks
5 cm/2 inch/piece of cucumber, cut into chunks
½ head of fennel
150 ml/¼ pint/⅔ cup water
125 ml/4 fl oz/½ cup Greek-style yogurt

Blend the kiwi fruit, cucumber, fennel and water until smooth. Then add the yogurt and blend for a few seconds.

Papaya and Fennel Smoothie

Use 2 papaya instead of the kiwi fruit. Cut them in half and scoop out their black seeds, then thinly peel the flesh and cut it into chunks. Purée as above, adding orange juice instead of water.

OTHER JUICE IDEAS

Banana and Ginger Milk

This is fabulously luxurious – it makes an irresistible snack or brilliant breakfast drink, providing energy to get the day under way and a contribution of calcium from the milk. Bananas are a terrific fruit for making creamy yet healthy concoctions that taste wicked. They are a great source of energy-giving carbohydrate and fibre, and they also provide potassium; ripe bananas are also regarded as being 'easy on the stomach' and unlikely to cause upsets. Ginger is known for helping to counteract nausea and aid digestion.

Serves 1

1 large banana, cut into chunks
1 piece of preserved stem ginger in syrup,
  drained and sliced
150 ml/¼ pint/⅔ cup milk

Blend the banana, ginger and milk until smooth. Pour into a glass and enjoy!

OTHER JUICE IDEAS

1 large mango, peeled, stoned (pitted) and cut into chunks
300 ml/½ pint/1¼ cups buttermilk
200 g/7 oz/1½ cups strawberries, stalks removed

Purée the mango with the buttermilk until smooth. Divide about half the buttermilk and mango mixture between 2 glasses. Then add the strawberries to the remaining mixture and purée until smooth. Add the strawberry mixture to the glasses, swirling with the mango drink.

Variation Yogurt can be used instead of the buttermilk.

Mango and Strawberry Swirl

This is thick, luscious and full of fresh fruit goodness as well as valuable dairy food value. Buttermilk is a low-fat dairy product, similar to skimmed milk, but with a creamy texture and slightly tangy flavour. It is a good source of calcium and provides valuable B vitamins. Buttermilk is ideal for making fruit smoothies as it does not curdle when puréed with fruit. (Milk curdles when mixed with straight fruit juice or purée unless the fruit is highly sweetened with sugar, almost to syrup proportion.) Traditionally, strawberries have a reputation as a cleansing fruit, good for the system and the liver. They contribute vitamin C to this drink and the mango also provides vitamin C along with beta carotene.

OTHER JUICE IDEAS

Strawberry Oat Crush

This is another smooth drink made without milk products. In addition to the fruit benefits from strawberries, the oats provide soluble fibre, which is thought to assist in restraining cholesterol levels. Frozen strawberries are terrific for this drink – part-thaw them for a few seconds in the microwave or leave them to stand until they are slightly softened so that they can be whizzed in a blender. This way they make an instant chilled drink.

Serves 1

150 g/5 oz/1 cup strawberries, stalks removed
3 tablespoons rolled oats
150 ml/¼ pint/⅔ cup water
honey, to taste (optional)

Purée the strawberries with the oats and water until smooth. Pour into a glass and stir in a little honey, to taste, if liked.

Berry Oat Crush Use fresh blackberries, raspberries, loganberries or blueberries instead of the strawberries. A mixture of berries can be used.

Healthy Storecupboard Snack
Keep rolled oats in stock to make a creamy drink when combined with frozen fruit. Frozen fruit and vegetables are full of goodness – they are frozen speedily after picking at their prime and often have a higher vitamin C content than fresh produce which may go through several days of packing, transporting and display before finally reaching the plate. Mixed summer, exotic or forest fruits are all ideal for making quick drinks. Many can be whizzed up from frozen or some of the harder fruit may need a few seconds in the microwave to soften it first.

OTHER JUICE IDEAS

Nutty Nectarine Whip

Serves 2

Variety is vital in a healthy diet. All food provides the body with the goodness it needs to survive and thrive, but no individual item should be eaten to excess. As well as eating lots of fruit, vegetables and starchy carbohydrates, it is important to include a variety of other ingredients for the goodness they offer. Nuts are a good example as they include the sort of fat that we should be including in the diet, plus vitamin E (a valuable antioxidant), vegetable protein and B vitamins. Including them in salads or hot vegetable dishes and adding them to breakfast cereal are good ways of including them in meals; they also bring excellent flavour and texture to fruit drinks. Pecan nuts have a soft texture which goes well with purées, but walnuts and almonds are also suitable nuts to include.

2 nectarines, halved, stoned (pitted) and cut into chunks
60 g/2 oz/½ cup shelled pecan nuts
grated rind and juice of 1 lime
3 tablespoons rolled oats
1 teaspoon honey or 2 teaspoons sugar
350 ml/12 fl oz/1½ cups water

Purée the nectarines, pecan nuts, lime rind and juice, oats and sugar with about a third of the water until smooth. Then gradually add the remaining water with the blender running.

Peach and Almond Whip Use peaches instead of nectarines, lemon instead of lime and almonds instead of pecan nuts.

OTHER JUICE IDEAS

Warming Infusions

Citrus and Ginger Ginseng

Apple and Orange Energizer

Golden Glow

East-West Apple Warmer

Minted Blackcurrant Cold Cure

Parsley and Pineapple Tisane

Elderflower Lemon Tisane

Aromatic Triple C

Camomile Apple Tea

Rosemary and Lime Tisane

Hot Banana Chocolate

Raspberry Honey Cup

Cherry Berry Punch

Citrus and Ginger Ginseng

Orange juice is usually included in cold drinks, but it is equally good in warm infusions, as here with ginseng and ginger. Ginseng is an ancient ingredient in oriental medicine. It is a stimulant and regarded as a tonic. Available in a mild form as a tisane, to be diluted with hot or cold water, it goes well with fruit juices. Combined with ginger it makes a warming drink and useful pick-me-up for helping to overcome fatigue and stress.

Serves 1

1 large orange
1 thin slice fresh root ginger, peeled
1 sachet ginseng tea
200 ml/7 fl oz/¾ cup boiling water
a little honey

Use a zester to remove the rind from the orange or grate it. Cut off all the peel and pith, then roughly chop the orange, discarding the pips. Purée the orange with the ginger. Place the ginseng tea in a mug and stir in the boiling water. Add the orange and stir in a little honey to taste.

Variation This makes a coarse-textured drink - for a fine drink, extract the juice from 1-2 oranges. Finely chop the ginger and add it to the ginseng with the boiling water. Then stir in the juice.

OTHER JUICE IDEAS

Apple and Orange Energizer

Restore your 'get-up-and-go' on cold winter days with this warming drink. With vitamin goodness from the fruit and the reputations of both rosemary and ginseng for boosting energy levels, it promotes a sense of well-being.

Serves 1

1 large fresh rosemary sprig
150 ml/¼ pint/⅔ cup boiling water
1 orange
1 large sweet dessert apple
1 sachet ginseng tea
a little honey (optional)

Place the rosemary in a mug and pour in the boiling water. Stir well, then add the ginseng tea and stir until it has dissolved. Extract the juice from the orange and apple, then stir it into the tea and drink while warm, adding a little honey if liked.

OTHER JUICE IDEAS

Serves 1

1 sachet ginseng tea
150 ml/¼ pint/⅔ cup boiling water
125 ml/4 fl oz/½ cup carrot juice
125 ml/4 fl oz/½ cup orange juice

Dissolve the ginseng in the boiling water. Stir in the carrot and orange juices and drink when warm.

Chilled Golden Glow This also tastes good when chilled. Dissolve the ginseng in the minimum of boiling water and top up with well-chilled juice.

Golden Glow

Orange and carrot juice taste fabulous with ginseng tea, bringing a sweet fruity flavour to its slightly spicy and musty flavour. With vitamin C and beta carotene, the drink makes a useful contribution to the diet as well as acting as a restorative.

OTHER JUICE IDEAS

Warm a mug or suitable glass with boiling water, then discard the water. Place the cinnamon and lemon rind in the mug or glass and add the boiling water. Stir in the ginseng tea until dissolved. Then stir in the apple juice and drink warm.

Variation For a spicier drink, heat the cinnamon and lemon with 200 ml/7 fl oz/¾ cup cold water in a small saucepan over a low heat. Keep the pan covered and allow plenty of time for the spice to infuse. Then bring to the boil. Remove from the heat and add the ginseng and apple, then heat gently for a few seconds, but do not allow to boil.

East-West Apple Warmer

Sweet, well-flavoured apple juice tastes terrific with ginseng tea, combining the traditional health-giving fruit of the West with the classic tonic of the East. Spiced with warming cinnamon, this drink is a welcome soother to counteract the horrid symptoms of a cold – a stuffy head and sore throat.

Serves 1

1 cinnamon stick
grated rind of 1 lemon
150 ml/¼ pint/⅔ cup boiling water
1 sachet ginseng tea
200 ml/7 fl oz/¾ cup apple juice

Minted Blackcurrant Cold Cure

Head-clearing, aromatic mint, throat-soothing honey and vitamin-rich blackcurrants help to combat colds in this warming drink. Sieve the blackcurrant juice if you want to remove the seeds, but leave it coarse to benefit from the fibre content of the fruit.

Serves 1

1 teaspoon honey
4 fresh mint sprigs
200 ml/7 fl oz/¾ cup boiling water
75 g/2½ oz/¾ cup blackcurrants
juice of 1 lemon

Rinse out a mug or glass with boiling water to warm it, then add the honey, mint and boiling water. Stir until the honey has dissolved. Purée the blackcurrants and lemon juice, then stir the purée into the mint infusion. Taste and add a little extra honey if liked.

OTHER JUICE IDEAS

Parsley and Pineapple Tisane

The fresh flavour of parsley and fruity pineapple go very well together. As a herbal remedy, parsley has a reputation for easing kidney and urinary tract problems. It is also a good breath-freshener and often combined with fresh garlic to reduce its lingering aroma. Pineapple provides some vitamin C and fibre; its age-old reputation is as an aid to digestion as well as being a fruit for soothing sore throats and assisting in the cure of many ailments. Puréeing and sieving, or extracting all the juice from, the trimmings off a fresh pineapple is a good way of making the most of the fruit.

Serves 1

8 fresh parsley sprigs
juice of 1 lemon
200 ml/7 fl oz/¾ cup boiling water
125 ml/4 fl oz/½ cup pineapple juice

Finely chop the parsley and mix with the lemon and boiling water in a warmed mug or glass. Stir in the pineapple juice.

OTHER JUICE IDEAS

Elderflower Lemon Tisane

Lemon juice provides vitamin C and it is known as a traditional cold cure, usually with honey to soothe a sore throat. The oils found in the rind of the lemon are thought to help the body fight infection, which is why it is important to include the rind as well as the juice in drinks.

2 heads of elderflowers
300 ml (½ pint) 1¼ cups boiling water
1 lemon
honey to taste

Select clean elderflowers and check them carefully for insects and debris, picking off any unwanted specimens. Then rinse the flowers lightly and shake off the water. Snip the tops of the heads off into a jug and pour on the boiling water. Stir well and cover to keep warm.

Use a zester to remove the rind from the lemon or grate it coarsely. Squeeze the juice from the fruit and mix with the rind in a warmed mug or glass. Stir the elderflower water, crushing the flowers, then strain it over the juice and stir in honey to taste.

OTHER JUICE IDEAS

Aromatic Triple C

Carrot, orange and red pepper make a drink rich in antioxidants and vitamin C. Cardamoms have a refreshing and head-clearing properties from their lemony, eucalyptus-like flavour and aroma. They go well with the sweet vegetables and orange in this warming pick-me-up.

Serves 1

1 large carrot
1 large orange
1 red (bell) pepper
2 green cardamoms
200 ml/7 fl oz/¾ cup boiling water

Extract the juice from the carrot, orange and pepper. Slit the cardamoms and scrape out the tiny black seeds into a mortar, then pound them to a powder with a pestle. Rinse out a mug or glass with boiling water to warm it. Place the ground cardamom in the warmed mug or glass and stir in the measured boiling water. Then stir in the prepared juice.

Camomile Apple Tea

Warming mace and fruity apple juice are combined with calming camomile in this soothing drink that goes down well on a cool evening, making a light alternative to a milk-based bedtime drink.

Serves 1

1 blade of mace
200 ml/7 fl oz/¾ cup water
1 sachet of camomile tea
150 ml/¼ pint/⅔ cup apple juice

Place the mace in a small saucepan and add the water. Bring slowly to the boil, then remove from the heat, cover and leave to infuse for 10 minutes. Bring back to the boil and pour over the camomile tea in a mug or glass. Leave to infuse for 2–3 minutes, then discard the tea bag and blade of mace. Stir in the apple juice.

OTHER JUICE IDEAS

Rosemary and Lime Tisane

A good alternative to morning coffee or tea, this tisane is both refreshing and stimulating.

Serves 1

1 lime
3 fresh rosemary sprigs
250 ml/8 fl oz/1 cup boiling water
sugar or honey to taste

Use a zester or coarse grater to remove the rind from the lime and place it in a mug or glass. Lightly crush the rosemary sprigs and add them to the lime rind, then pour in the boiling water. Cover and leave to infuse for about 3 minutes. Meanwhile, squeeze the juice from the lime and stir it into the tisane with sugar or honey to taste.

OTHER JUICE IDEAS

Hot Banana Chocolate

Instead of drinking very sweet, sugary and high-fat commercial chocolate drinks, try this wonderful hot banana milk flavoured with cocoa. The sweetness of the banana is sufficient to flavour the drink, so there is no need for added sugar, and it also contributes potassium and fibre to the calcium, protein, B vitamins, phosphorus and zinc found in milk. While fostering a craving for chocolate is not a good thing, making home-made alternatives to sugary commercial products is a real plus.

Serves 1

1 teaspoon cocoa
250 ml/8 fl oz/1 cup milk
1 small banana

Blend the cocoa, a little of the milk and the banana to a purée. Bring the remaining milk to the boil, then pour it into the banana purée and whizz until smooth and frothy. Pour into a mug or glass and serve at once.

OTHER JUICE IDEAS

Raspberry Honey Cup

Raspberries have a reputation for being a cleansing fruit, good for detoxifying the system as well as for their vitamin C content. As well as making superb summer drinks they taste fabulous in this creamy oat drink, which makes a warming snack on cold days.

Serves 1

60 g/2 oz/⅔ cup raspberries
1 teaspoon honey
3 tablespoons rolled oats
200 ml/7 fl oz/¾ cup boiling water

Purée the raspberries with the honey and oats until smooth. Gradually pour in the boiling water with the blender running, then pour the drink into a glass or mug and serve.

OTHER JUICE IDEAS

Place the cinnamon stick in a small saucepan. Add the apple juice, cover and heat gently, stirring occasionally, for 5 minutes, without allowing the juice to boil. Uncover the pan and bring the juice just to the boil, then remove it from the heat and discard the cinnamon stick. Blend the cherries and blueberries with the hot apple juice and pour or strain into a mug or glass, pressing all the juice from the fruit if straining the drink. Serve warm.

Cherry Berry Punch

Cherries are known as a fruit for easing gout and, like other fruit, for their general system-cleansing properties. Combined with naturally sweet blueberries, a fruit known for its anti-bacterial properties, they make a wonderfully fruity hot drink.

Serves 1

1 cinnamon stick
200 ml/7 fl oz/¾ cup apple juice
60 g/2 oz/¾ cup cherries, stoned
60 g/2 oz/¾ cup blueberries

OTHER JUICE IDEAS

Sweet Dishes

Apple and Apricot Oaty

Exotic Pear Oaty

Fragrant Cranberry Jelly

Spiced Orange Jelly

Mango Sorbet

Blackcurrant and Banana Freeze

OTHER JUICE IDEAS

Apple and Apricot Oaty

If you are not much of a morning person but bored with the usual breakfast cereals, put this mixture to soak in the refrigerator last thing at night and you will be greeted with a delicious fruit porridge in the morning. It is a cross between porridge and muesli, and the apricot juice provides beta carotene and vitamin C. Serve topped with fresh fruit salad or sliced banana to make a substantial, fibre-rich breakfast.

Serves 1

125 ml/4 fl oz/½ cup apple juice
125 ml/4 fl oz/½ cup apricot juice
125 g (4 oz) 1½ cups rolled oats

Mix the fruit juices in a deep bowl or basin and stir in the oats. Cover and leave to soak for about 5 hours or overnight. Stir well before serving.

Sherried Fruit Cream

Add 2 tablespoons dry sherry and stir in 150 ml/¼ pint/⅔ cup yogurt. Divide between 2 dishes and top with raspberries or other fresh fruit to make a tempting dessert.

OTHER JUICE IDEAS

Exotic Pear Cream

This is another healthy sweet dish, full of
fibre from the pears, whole lime and oats
as well as vitamin C. The walnuts add
depth of flavour and they are thought to
help prevent heart disease when eaten in
small quantities. Serve cream for breakfast
or as a simple dessert.

Serves 4

1 lime
4 pears, peeled, cored and cut into chunks
45 g/1½ oz/⅓ cup walnuts
2 pieces preserved stem ginger in syrup, drained
125 g/4 oz/1½ cups rolled oats
300 ml/½ pint/1¼ cupsmild plain yogurt

Cut the lime in half, then cut it into small
pieces, discarding any pips. Place the pieces
of lime in a blender. Add the pears,
walnuts and ginger. Purée the pear and
lime mixture until smooth, then turn it into
a bowl and stir in the oats. Cover and leave
to stand for 2 hours or longer. Stir in the
yogurt and serve.

OTHER JUICE IDEAS

Fragrant Cranberry Jelly

This makes a brilliant alternative to rich puddings at Christmas or any other time of the year when you have cranberries in the freezer. Use a juicer to extract the juice from the cranberries and to avoid having to sieve the liquid. Cranberries are a super-rich source of vitamin C.

Serves 4

1 tablespoon powdered gelatine

4 tablespoons cold water

250 g/9 oz/2¼ cups cranberries

500 ml/17 fl oz/2¼ red grape juice

2 tablespoons sugar

2 teaspoons rosewater

whipped cream, fromage frais or yogurt to serve

Cranberry and Apple Drink
Blend 125 g/4 oz/1 cup cranberries with 200 ml/7 fl oz/¾ cup sweet apple juice to make a deliciously tangy fruit drink. Use a juicer to make smooth cranberry juice or press the juice through a sieve. However, the pips and skins from the cranberries are a good source of fibre and once you are used to drinking coarse purées, they are not at all objectionable.

Raspberry and Grape Jelly
Use raspberries instead of cranberries and reduce or omit the sugar to taste. Strain the liquid as above to remove the pips or leave it coarse for an everyday dessert.

Sprinkle the gelatine over the water in a small heatproof bowl or basin. Do not stir but set the gelatine aside to sponge – it will absorb the water, swell and look spongy.

Purée the cranberries with the grape juice in a blender, then strain the liquid through a sieve into a bowl. Press and scrape the pulp to extract as much purée as possible from it, discarding the tough skins and pips at the end. Stir in the sugar and rosewater.

Stand the bowl of sponged gelatine over a small saucepan of hot water until it has dissolved. Stir the gelatine liquid occasionally – it is ready when it is clear and smooth. Stir in a little of the juice, then pour it into the main batch of juice, stirring continuously. Divide between 4 glass dishes and chill until set. Serve topped with whipped cream, fromage frais or yogurt.

Spiced Orange Jelly

This is one of my favourite simple desserts. It is light and interesting, and a good alternative to rich desserts or over-familiar fruit salad at the end of a dinner party. Pour it over fresh fruit, such as raspberries or strawberries, for extra vitamins and phytochemicals, then serve with a little yogurt.

Serves 4

1 cinnamon stick
6 cloves
200 ml/7 fl oz/¾ cup water
5 teaspoons powdered gelatine
5 large juicy oranges
caster sugar to taste

Place the cinnamon stick and cloves in a small saucepan. Add the water and heat gently until the water comes to a full bubbling boil. Remove from the heat, stir well, then cover and leave to stand until completely cold.

Remove the spices from the water. Sprinkle the gelatine over and heat gently, stirring occasionally, until it has dissolved completely. Make sure there are no grains of gelatine stuck to the side of the pan.

Finely grate the rind from 2 oranges and add it to the gelatine liquid. Squeeze the juice from the oranges and stir into the gelatine liquid. Add sugar to taste and stir until it has dissolved, then pour the jelly into a dish. Cover and chill until set.

OTHER JUICE IDEAS

Mango Sorbet

Home-made sorbet may be sweet, but it is far less so than bought sorbets. It also provides nutrients from the fresh fruit – vitamin C and beta carotene from the mango.

Serves 6

5 tablespoon sugar
125 ml/4 fl oz/½ cup water
grated rind and juice of 3 lemons
600 ml/1 pint/2½ cups mango juice

Place the sugar in a saucepan and add the water. Heat gently, stirring, until the sugar has dissolved completely, then bring the syrup to the boil. Remove the pan from the heat. Add the lemon rind and juice, then stir in the mango juice.

Pour the mixture into a freezer container and freeze until the mixture begins to form ice around the edges. (This takes about 3 hours.) Turn the mixture into a food processor and process until smooth, then replace it in the container and freeze again. Repeat twice, whizzing the mixture until smooth on each occasion. By the third time, the sorbet should be opaque and smooth – leave it in the freezer for a final 3 hours or more, until firm, before serving.

If the sorbet is frozen overnight or longer and becomes quite hard, transfer it to the refrigerator about 15 minutes before serving so that it softens slightly and is easier to scoop out.

OTHER JUICE IDEAS

Blackcurrant and Banana Freeze

Bananas and yogurt make a delicious and simple ice cream that is a healthy alternative to commercial types made with lots of sugar and/or with a very high fat content. Blackcurrant juice brings a wonderful rich flavour and lots of vitamin C to this healthy treat.

Serves 4

200 ml/7 fl oz/¾ cup blackcurrant juice
2 tablespoons icing (confectioner's) sugar
3 bananas
300 ml/½ pint/1¼ cups Greek-style yogurt

Purée the blackcurrant juice, icing sugar and bananas until smooth, then add the yogurt and mix briefly. Turn the mixture into a freezer container and freeze until ice forms around the edge. (This will take 2—3 hours.) Process the mixture until smooth in a food processor, then return it to the container and freeze again. Repeat once more, then freeze until firm.

INDEX

INDEX

INDEX

INDEX